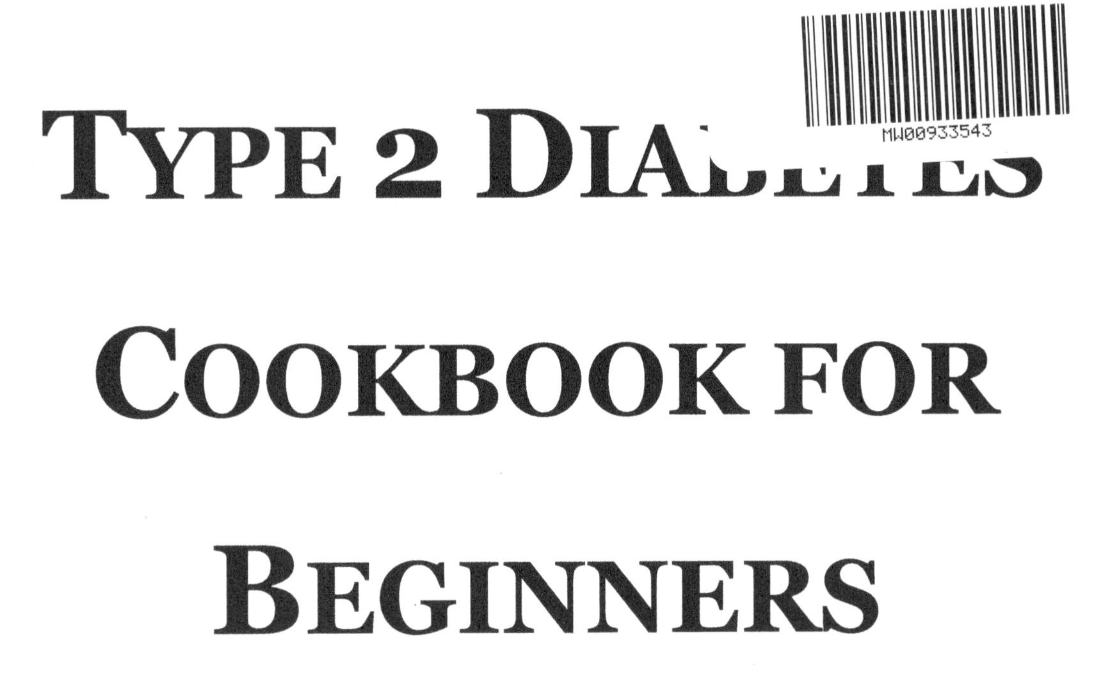

TYPE 2 DIABETES COOKBOOK FOR BEGINNERS

1800 Days of Recipes, Tasty, Quick and Easy to Prepare. Includes a 45-Day Meal Plan

Elara Vindelis

Table of Contents

PART I: INTRODUCTION TO TYPE 2 DIABETES AND NUTRITION 11

1. WELCOME TO YOUR JOURNEY 11

Introduction to the Cookbook 11

How This Book Can Help You 12

2. UNDERSTANDING TYPE 2 DIABETES 14

Basics of Type 2 Diabetes 14

Impact of Diet on Diabetes Management 16

3. NUTRITIONAL GUIDANCE FOR TYPE 2 DIABETES 17

Macronutrients and Their Roles 17

The Importance of Fiber and Whole Foods 19

Reading and Understanding Food Labels 21

PART II: RECIPE CHAPTERS 23

4. BREAKFASTS TO START YOUR DAY RIGHT 23

Energizing Smoothies and Juices 23

1. MORNING GLOW SMOOTHIE 23
2. BLUEBERRY OMEGA BOOST 23
3. GREEN DETOX JUICE 24
4. PROTEIN-PACKED CHOCOLATE ALMOND SMOOTHIE 24

Hearty Oatmeals and Porridges 25

1. COCONUT CHIA OATMEAL 25
2. ALMOND BERRY PORRIDGE 25
3. SAVORY MISO OATMEAL 26
4. APPLE CINNAMON PROTEIN OATMEAL 26
5. PUMPKIN SPICE PORRIDGE 27
6. CHOCOLATE PEANUT BUTTER BANANA OATMEAL 27

Protein-Packed Eggs and Breakfast Meats 28

1. SPINACH AND FETA OMELETTE 28
2. TURKEY BACON AND EGG MUFFINS 28
3. AVOCADO AND EGG BREAKFAST WRAP 29
4. SMOKED SALMON AND CREAM CHEESE SCRAMBLE 29
5. CHICKEN SAUSAGE AND VEGETABLE SKILLET 30

5. NOURISHING LUNCHES 31

Quick and Easy Salads ... *31*
1. SUMMER BERRY SPINACH SALAD ... 31
2. CRISP CUCUMBER AND RADISH SALAD ... 31
3. AVOCADO AND BLACK BEAN SALAD ... 32
Warm and Comforting Soups ... *32*
1. TUSCAN WHITE BEAN SOUP ... 32
2. CLASSIC CHICKEN NOODLE SOUP ... 33
3. ROASTED BUTTERNUT SQUASH SOUP ... 33
4. SPICY LENTIL AND TOMATO SOUP ... 34
5. BROCCOLI AND CHEDDAR SOUP ... 34
6. SWEET POTATO AND GINGER SOUP ... 35
Sandwiches and Wraps for On-the-Go ... *36*
1. GRILLED VEGETABLE AND HUMMUS WRAP ... 36
2. TURKEY AND AVOCADO CLUB SANDWICH ... 36
3. CHICKPEA SALAD SANDWICH ... 37
4. SPICY TUNA WRAP ... 37
5. ROASTED VEGETABLE AND GOAT CHEESE PANINI ... 38
6. CHICKEN CAESAR SALAD WRAP ... 38
6. SATISFYING DINNERS ... 41
Vegetable-Forward Dishes ... *41*
1. ROASTED CAULIFLOWER STEAKS WITH TAHINI SAUCE ... 41
2. ZUCCHINI NOODLES WITH AVOCADO PESTO ... 41
3. SWEET POTATO AND BLACK BEAN BOWL ... 42
Lean Meats and Seafood ... *42*
1. HERB-CRUSTED SALMON ... 42
2. LEMON GARLIC CHICKEN BREASTS ... 43
3. SPICED TURKEY MEATBALLS ... 43
Creative Pasta and Rice Alternatives ... *44*
1. CAULIFLOWER RICE STIR-FRY ... 44
2. ZUCCHINI NOODLE PESTO ... 44
3. BUTTERNUT SQUASH LASAGNA ... 45
4. SPAGHETTI SQUASH PAD THAI ... 45
5. BROCCOLI RICE CASSEROLE ... 46
7. SNACKS AND SIDES ... 49

Healthy Snack Ideas *49*
1. CRISPY CHICKPEA AND EDAMAME SNACK 49
2. AVOCADO AND COTTAGE CHEESE STUFFED CHERRY TOMATOES 49
3. SWEET POTATO TOAST WITH ALMOND BUTTER AND BANANA 50
4. KALE CHIPS WITH NUTRITIONAL YEAST 50
5. PEANUT BUTTER ENERGY BALLS 51
6. BAKED APPLE CHIPS 51
Vegetable Sides *52*
1. GARLIC PARMESAN ROASTED BRUSSELS SPROUTS 52
2. MAPLE GLAZED CARROTS 52
3. SPICY ROASTED CAULIFLOWER 53
Whole Grain and Legume Sides *53*
1. QUINOA TABBOULEH 53
2. LEMON GARLIC LENTILS 54
3. BARLEY AND MUSHROOM PILAF 54
4. BLACK BEAN AND CORN SALAD 55
5. FARRO WITH ROASTED VEGETABLES 55
6. MEDITERRANEAN LENTIL SALAD 56
8. DESSERTS WITHOUT THE GUILT 57
Fruit-Based Desserts *57*
1. BAKED CINNAMON APPLES 57
2. MANGO AND CHIA PUDDING 57
3. PEACHES GRILLED WITH HONEY AND YOGURT 58
Low-Sugar Baked Goods *58*
1. ALMOND FLOUR BLUEBERRY MUFFINS 58
2. WHOLE WHEAT BANANA BREAD 59
3. OATMEAL PUMPKIN MUFFINS 59
Sweet Snacks *60*
1. NO-BAKE CHOCOLATE PEANUT BUTTER ENERGY BALLS 60
2. BAKED APPLE CHIPS WITH CINNAMON 60
3. FROZEN YOGURT BERRIES 61
4. ALMOND AND DATE TRUFFLES 61
5. GREEK YOGURT AND HONEY DIPPED GRAPES 62
6. PEANUT BUTTER BANANA ROLL-UPS 62

9. Drinks for Every Occasion 65
Herbal Teas and Infusions 65
1. SOOTHING LAVENDER TEA 65
2. GINGER TURMERIC TEA 65
3. PEPPERMINT LEAF TEA 65
4. HIBISCUS AND ROSEHIP TEA 66
5. TURMERIC AND CINNAMON INFUSION 66
6. GREEN TEA WITH MINT AND LIME 67
Low-Sugar Beverages 67
1. BERRY ANTIOXIDANT SMOOTHIE 67
2. GREEN DETOX SMOOTHIE 67
3. PROTEIN-PACKED PEANUT BUTTER SMOOTHIE 68
Nutritious Smoothies 68
1. TROPICAL MORNING SMOOTHIE 68
2. ANTIOXIDANT BERRY WALNUT SMOOTHIE 69
3. SPINACH AVOCADO GREEN SMOOTHIE 69
4. SUNRISE CITRUS AND CARROT SMOOTHIE 69
5. CREAMY BLUEBERRY OATMEAL SMOOTHIE 70
6. PEACH GINGER DETOX SMOOTHIE 70
10. Special Occasions 73
Festive Meals and How to Approach Them 73
1. ROASTED BUTTERNUT SQUASH WITH CRANBERRY QUINOA STUFFING .. 73
2. HONEY GLAZED HAM WITH CLOVES AND ORANGE JUICE 73
3. MEDITERRANEAN STUFFED BELL PEPPERS 74
4. GARLIC AND HERB ROASTED TURKEY BREAST 74
5. WILD RICE AND CRANBERRY PILAF 75
Healthy Holiday Treats 75
1. GINGERBREAD OATMEAL COOKIES 75
2. CHOCOLATE PEPPERMINT ENERGY BALLS 76
3. PUMPKIN SPICE MINI MUFFINS 76
Entertaining with Diabetes-Friendly Dishes 77
1. ZUCCHINI NOODLES WITH AVOCADO PESTO 77
2. QUINOA SALAD WITH BLACK BEANS AND MANGO 77
3. BAKED SALMON WITH DIJON CRUST 78

PART III: 45-DAY MEAL PLAN **79**

11. 45-Day Meal Plan 79

Weekly Shopping Lists *79*

Daily Meal Planning Guide *81*

Tips for Meal Prepping *83*

MEASUREMENT CONVERSION TABLE **85**

PART IV: BEYOND THE KITCHEN **87**

12. Living with Type 2 Diabetes 87

Lifestyle Tips for Managing Diabetes *87*

Exercise Recommendations *88*

Stress Management Techniques *90*

13. Conclusion and Resources 93

Continuing Your Journey *93*

Further Reading and Online Resources *94*

Support Groups and Communities *96*

APPENDICES **99**

A. Glossary of Terms 99

B. Substitution Chart for Common Ingredients 101

C. Nutritional Information Guide 103

PART I: INTRODUCTION TO TYPE 2 DIABETES AND NUTRITION

1. WELCOME TO YOUR JOURNEY

INTRODUCTION TO THE COOKBOOK

Welcome to a journey that promises to transform not just your meals, but your approach to managing Type 2 diabetes. If you're holding this book, you might be seeking a change—a way to balance your blood sugar levels, incorporate healthful eating into your busy life, and enjoy delicious meals that please both diabetic and non-diabetic family members. You're in the right place.

This cookbook is more than a collection of recipes; it's a guide, designed to empower you to make informed dietary choices without sacrificing flavor or convenience. It's about finding joy in cooking and eating, knowing that every dish you prepare is a step toward better health.

I understand the challenges you face. Time is precious, and the last thing you need is complicated meal prep that takes away from family time. You may also be navigating the vast sea of nutrition advice, trying to discern what's best for managing diabetes. It can feel overwhelming. That's why this book aims to simplify the process, providing clear, easy-to-follow recipes that cater to your health needs and taste preferences.

Each recipe has been crafted with care, keeping in mind the nutritional guidelines that are important for managing Type 2 diabetes. But more than that, these recipes are designed for real life. They're for those evenings when you're tired after work and need something quick and satisfying, for the mornings when you want a breakfast that will keep your energy levels steady, and for the special occasions that call for something festive yet healthful.

You'll find that we don't compromise on variety or flavor. From comforting soups and hearty salads to flavorful main dishes and tempting desserts, there's something for every palate and occasion. The ingredients used are accessible and often already in your pantry, and the methods are straightforward, making healthy cooking achievable for everyone, regardless of culinary skill.

As we embark on this culinary journey together, I want you to know that you're not alone. Consider me your partner in the kitchen—a friend who's here to support you, offer tips, and share in the joys of your successes. I encourage you to experiment with the recipes, adapting them to your preferences and dietary needs. Cooking is a personal journey, one that allows for creativity and personal growth.

In addition to the recipes, this cookbook offers a glimpse into the importance of nutrition in managing Type 2 diabetes. It's essential to understand how food affects your blood sugar levels and overall health, but this knowledge should not be a source of stress. Instead, I hope to provide clarity and a sense of confidence as you make choices about what to eat.

Remember, managing diabetes through diet does not mean you have to give up the foods you love. It's about balance, moderation, and making informed choices. It's about finding ways to enjoy your meals while keeping your health in mind. This cookbook is designed to help you do just that, offering delicious, diabetes-friendly alternatives to your favorite dishes.

As you try the recipes, you'll also learn more about the principles of a balanced diabetic diet—how to incorporate a variety of nutrients into your meals, the importance of fiber, and the role of carbohydrates, proteins, and fats. These are not just guidelines but tools that will empower you to take control of your health.

Moreover, this cookbook is about building a healthy relationship with food. It's about understanding that food is not just fuel but a source of pleasure and nourishment. It's about making choices that benefit your body and soul, creating meals that bring joy and satisfaction.

I invite you to use this cookbook not just as a resource for recipes but as a companion on your journey to better health. Let it be a source of inspiration, a guide to healthier eating, and a reminder that managing Type 2 diabetes can be a delicious endeavor.

In closing, I want to emphasize that every step you take towards healthier eating is a positive one. There will be challenges and setbacks, but there will also be victories and moments of joy. Celebrate your successes, learn from your experiences, and keep moving forward.

This journey is not just about managing diabetes; it's about embracing a lifestyle that promotes overall well-being. It's about making choices that support your health and happiness, and it's a journey that I am honored to share with you.

Let's begin this culinary adventure together, with open hearts and appetites ready for the delicious, healthful meals that await us. Welcome to your journey towards a healthier, happier life.

How This Book Can Help You

Empowerment Through Knowledge and Flavor

First and foremost, this cookbook empowers you with knowledge. Understanding the impact of food on your blood sugar levels and overall health is crucial. But this knowledge doesn't have to be a limitation. Instead, it opens up a new world of flavors and possibilities. Through the pages of this book, you'll learn how to navigate your kitchen and your diet with confidence, transforming the way you think about food and its role in your life.

Recipes That Bring People Together

One of the book's core beliefs is that meals should bring joy and people together, not separate plates for those managing diabetes and everyone else. The recipes within these pages are carefully crafted to be enjoyed by all members of the family, diabetic or not. This inclusivity is key to creating a supportive and stress-free mealtime environment.

Simplifying Healthy Eating

Time is a precious commodity, and this book respects that. The recipes are designed to fit into your busy life, with straightforward instructions and ingredients that are easy to find. You won't need to spend hours in the kitchen to prepare a healthful meal. Instead, you'll discover the joy of quick, simple dishes that are as nourishing as they are delicious.

A 45-Day Meal Plan: Your Roadmap to Success

One of the most daunting aspects of managing diabetes through diet can be figuring out where to start. To help you on this journey, the book includes a comprehensive 45-day meal plan. This plan serves as a roadmap, offering a structured approach to your meals and simplifying the process of planning, shopping, and cooking. It's designed not just for individual days but as a guide to developing long-term, sustainable eating habits.

Beyond Recipes: A Holistic Approach

Managing diabetes extends beyond just what you eat. It's about adopting a lifestyle that supports your health and well-being. That's why this book also touches on other aspects of diabetes management, such as exercise and stress reduction. These sections aim to provide a holistic approach to your health, complementing the dietary advice and recipes with tips for incorporating physical activity and relaxation into your routine.

A Source of Inspiration and Support

At its heart, this book is a source of inspiration and support. It's here to remind you that a diagnosis of Type 2 diabetes is not the end of enjoying food. Instead, it's an opportunity to explore new flavors, ingredients, and ways of cooking. The book aims to be a companion on your journey, offering encouragement and practical advice every step of the way.

Making Informed Choices

As you become more familiar with the principles of diabetes-friendly nutrition, you'll find yourself making informed choices with ease. This book aims to demystify food labels, explain the importance of macronutrients, and guide you in making adjustments that suit your individual needs. It's about gaining the confidence to make choices that are right for you, without feeling restricted or overwhelmed.

Celebrating Every Success

Every meal you prepare, every new habit you adopt, is a step forward on your journey. This book encourages you to celebrate these successes, no matter how small they may seem. It's these moments of achievement that build confidence and motivation, fueling your continued progress towards better health.

Your Partner in Health

Consider this book your partner in health. It's here to guide, to inspire, and to support you. The journey of managing diabetes through diet is a personal one, and this book respects that. It provides the tools and knowledge you need, but also encourages you to listen to your body and make adjustments as necessary. After all, you are the expert on your own body and life.

A Journey of Discovery

Ultimately, this book is about discovery. You'll discover new foods, new flavors, and new joys in cooking and eating. You'll also discover strength you might not have known you had—the strength to make positive changes, to adapt, and to thrive. Managing diabetes through diet is a journey, but it's one that you don't have to make alone.

2. Understanding Type 2 Diabetes

Basics of Type 2 Diabetes

Type 2 diabetes is a condition that affects millions of people worldwide, yet its basics are often misunderstood. Understanding this condition is the first step towards effective management and a healthier life. So, let's demystify Type 2 diabetes together, breaking down the complexities into understandable pieces.

At its core, Type 2 diabetes is characterized by a problem with insulin, a hormone produced by the pancreas. Insulin acts like a key, opening the doors of our cells so glucose (sugar) from the food we eat can enter and be converted into energy. In Type 2 diabetes, this process doesn't work as it should. The cells become resistant to insulin, meaning glucose stays in the bloodstream, leading to high blood sugar levels.

Why does this insulin resistance happen? The answer isn't simple, as multiple factors contribute to the development of Type 2 diabetes. Genetics play a role; if you have family members with diabetes, your risk increases. However, lifestyle factors such as poor diet, lack of physical activity, and being overweight are significant contributors that can tip the scales from risk to reality.

High blood sugar levels over time can lead to various health issues, affecting almost every part of the body. It can damage blood vessels, leading to heart disease, affect the kidneys, eyes, and nerves, and even impact mental health. The good news is that with the right strategies, the effects of Type 2 diabetes can be managed, and in some cases, reversed.

Diagnosis is a critical step, often achieved through a simple blood test to measure glucose levels. If you're diagnosed, it's natural to feel a range of emotions, from disbelief to determination.

Accepting the diagnosis as a call to action can be empowering, turning it into an opportunity to embrace healthier habits.

The management of Type 2 diabetes revolves around maintaining blood sugar levels within a healthy range. This is where diet plays a crucial role. Contrary to common belief, this doesn't mean adhering to a restrictive, joyless eating plan. Instead, it's about finding balance, understanding the impact of different foods on blood sugar, and making informed choices that satisfy both your palate and your nutritional needs.

Physical activity is another pillar of diabetes management. Regular exercise helps improve insulin sensitivity, meaning the body can use insulin more effectively to lower blood sugar levels. Plus, physical activity has the added benefits of weight management, improved mood, and overall better health.

Medication may also be part of the management strategy. For some, lifestyle changes alone aren't enough to keep blood sugar levels in check. Medications can help, and they come in various forms, from pills to insulin injections. The key is to work closely with your healthcare team to find the right combination of treatments that work for you.

Monitoring blood sugar levels is essential. It provides immediate feedback on how well your management strategies are working and can help you make adjustments as needed. Whether it's through a traditional blood glucose meter or a continuous glucose monitor, keeping track of your levels can help you maintain better control.

Education is power, especially when it comes to managing Type 2 diabetes. Understanding how different aspects of your lifestyle affect your blood sugar levels empowers you to make choices that support your health. This book aims to be part of your education, providing you with the knowledge and tools you need to navigate your journey with confidence.

Living with Type 2 diabetes means adapting to changes, but it doesn't have to limit your life. It's about making mindful choices, understanding your body, and taking steps to manage your health proactively. It's a journey of discovery, learning not just about diabetes, but about yourself, your strengths, and your capacity for positive change.

Remember, you're not alone on this journey. A supportive community, whether it's online, in person, or through the pages of this book, can provide encouragement, share experiences, and offer valuable advice. Sharing your story can also be incredibly powerful, both for you and for others who are walking a similar path.

Finally, managing Type 2 diabetes is an ongoing process. There will be challenges and setbacks, but also successes and breakthroughs. Celebrate your achievements, learn from the obstacles, and keep moving forward. With the right approach, Type 2 diabetes can be a manageable part of your life, not a defining characteristic.

As we delve deeper into this book, we'll explore the nutritional strategies and lifestyle changes that can help you manage Type 2 diabetes effectively. From understanding the glycemic index to discovering delicious, diabetes-friendly recipes, you'll find tools and inspiration to help you live well with diabetes. Together, we'll navigate the journey towards better health, armed with knowledge, supported by a community, and inspired by the possibilities of a vibrant, healthful life.

Impact of Diet on Diabetes Management

A foundational concept in the dietary management of diabetes is the glycemic index (GI), a scale that ranks carbohydrate-containing foods by how much they raise blood glucose levels compared to pure glucose. Foods with a high GI are rapidly digested and absorbed, causing a quicker and higher rise in blood sugar levels. Conversely, foods with a low GI are digested and absorbed more slowly, leading to a gradual rise in blood sugar levels.

However, the GI tells only part of the story. The glycemic load (GL) also plays a crucial role. GL considers the GI of a food and the carbohydrate content in a serving size, giving a more comprehensive picture of how a food might impact blood sugar levels. Understanding these concepts can guide you in making informed choices about the carbohydrates you include in your diet.

Carbohydrates are often demonized in discussions about diabetes, but it's important to differentiate between the types of carbohydrates. Whole grains, fruits, vegetables, and legumes, which are high in fiber, have a different effect on blood sugar levels than refined carbohydrates found in processed foods, sugary drinks, and sweets.

Incorporating a variety of high-fiber, low-GI foods into your diet can help slow the absorption of glucose into your bloodstream, preventing spikes in blood sugar levels. Moreover, these foods can contribute to a sense of fullness, helping with weight management—a crucial aspect of diabetes management.

While carbohydrates receive much of the attention in diabetes management, fats, and proteins play significant roles. Healthy fats, such as those found in avocados, nuts, seeds, and oily fish, can help slow the absorption of carbohydrates, reducing spikes in blood sugar. Meanwhile, proteins have minimal impact on blood sugar levels and can help maintain muscle mass, which is important for metabolism.

Choosing lean protein sources and healthy fats while limiting saturated and trans fats can support not only blood sugar control but also cardiovascular health, which is particularly important for individuals with diabetes.

Consistency in meal timing can also profoundly impact blood sugar control. Eating regular meals and snacks helps prevent the peaks and valleys in blood sugar levels that can occur with irregular eating patterns. It also supports effective use of insulin and diabetes medications.

Dietary management of diabetes doesn't stop with what's on your plate. Hydration, for example, plays a key role in maintaining blood sugar levels. Water does not directly lower blood sugar levels, but it helps eliminate excess glucose through urine and prevents dehydration.

Additionally, mindful eating practices can enhance your relationship with food. By paying attention to hunger cues, eating slowly, and enjoying each bite, you can improve your satiety from meals and avoid overeating, which is beneficial for blood sugar control and weight management.

One of the most empowering aspects of dietary management in diabetes is the ability to personalize your approach. There is no one-size-fits-all diet for diabetes; what works for one person may not work for another. This is where working with a registered dietitian or certified diabetes educator can be invaluable. They can help you tailor your diet to your specific needs, preferences, and lifestyle, ensuring that it is both effective for managing your diabetes and enjoyable.

Adopting a diabetes-friendly diet is not about deprivation; it's a journey of discovery. It's an opportunity to explore new foods, experiment with recipes, and find joy in nourishing your body. Remember, small, sustainable changes are more effective than overhauls that feel restrictive and daunting.

In navigating your dietary journey, patience and self-compassion are key. Changes don't happen overnight, and there will be challenges along the way. Celebrate your successes, learn from your experiences, and know that each step forward is a step toward better health.

The impact of diet on diabetes management cannot be overstated. It is a powerful tool in your arsenal, offering the ability to significantly influence your blood sugar levels, reduce your risk of diabetes-related complications, and enhance your overall quality of life. By understanding the basics of nutrition, embracing a balanced and personalized approach to eating, and viewing dietary changes as opportunities for growth and discovery, you can take control of your diabetes and embark on a path to a healthier, happier you.

3. Nutritional Guidance for Type 2 Diabetes

Macronutrients and Their Roles

Carbohydrates: The Energy Source

Carbohydrates are often the main focus in diabetes management due to their direct impact on blood sugar levels. They are the body's primary energy source, broken down into glucose, which fuels our cells. However, not all carbs are created equal. They can be categorized into two main types: simple and complex.

Simple carbohydrates are quickly absorbed by the body, causing rapid spikes in blood sugar. These are found in sugary foods and drinks, as well as processed foods. On the other hand, complex carbohydrates take longer to break down, leading to a more gradual increase in blood sugar. These are found in whole grains, legumes, vegetables, and fruits.

The key to managing diabetes doesn't lie in eliminating carbohydrates but in choosing the right types and amounts. Emphasizing complex carbohydrates, particularly those high in fiber, can help maintain stable blood sugar levels and support overall health.

Proteins: The Building Blocks

Proteins are crucial for building and repairing tissues, making enzymes and hormones, and supporting immune function. Unlike carbohydrates, proteins have a minimal impact on blood sugar levels, making them a key component of a diabetes-friendly diet.

Including a source of lean protein at each meal can help maintain muscle mass, which is important for metabolism and weight management. Choices like fish, poultry, legumes, tofu, and low-fat dairy products can provide the protein your body needs without the excess saturated fats that can contribute to heart disease—a concern for those with diabetes.

Fats: The Misunderstood Macronutrient

Fats have often been villainized, but they're essential for absorbing vitamins, protecting our organs, and providing long-lasting energy. The trick is to focus on the type of fat rather than eliminating fat altogether.

Monounsaturated and polyunsaturated fats are known as "good" fats. They can improve blood cholesterol levels, decreasing the risk of heart disease. Sources include avocados, nuts, seeds, and fish. Saturated and trans fats, found in red meat, butter, and processed foods, should be limited. These "bad" fats can raise cholesterol levels and increase the risk of heart disease.

Balancing Macronutrients for Diabetes Management

Balancing these macronutrients is critical in managing Type 2 diabetes. A balanced plate that includes complex carbohydrates, lean protein, and healthy fats can provide the nutrients your body needs without causing undesirable spikes in blood sugar levels.

It's also important to consider the timing and consistency of meals. Eating regular, balanced meals can help maintain steady blood sugar levels throughout the day. Incorporating a variety of foods not only ensures you're getting a broad range of nutrients but also keeps meals interesting and enjoyable.

Listening to Your Body

Understanding macronutrients and their roles is just the beginning. Each person's body responds differently to different foods. What works for one person may not work for another, making it essential to listen to your body and adjust your diet based on how foods affect your blood sugar levels.

Keeping a food diary can be a helpful tool. By tracking what you eat and how it impacts your blood sugar readings, you can identify patterns and make informed decisions about your diet. This personalized approach is key to managing diabetes effectively.

The Role of a Healthcare Team

Working with a healthcare team, including a registered dietitian or certified diabetes educator, can provide valuable guidance in understanding macronutrients and tailoring your diet to your specific needs. They can help you design a meal plan that balances macronutrients effectively, ensuring you're getting the nutrition you need while managing your blood sugar levels.

A Journey of Discovery

Embracing a balanced diet rich in healthy macronutrients is not just about managing diabetes; it's about discovering a world of nutritious and delicious foods that can enhance your overall well-being. It's an opportunity to explore new recipes, experiment with different ingredients, and enjoy meals that nourish both your body and soul.

Remember, managing diabetes through diet is a journey, not a destination. It's about making continuous adjustments, learning from your experiences, and finding joy in the process. With knowledge, patience, and a dash of creativity, you can create a diet that supports your health goals and brings satisfaction to your taste buds.

The Importance of Fiber and Whole Foods

Fiber is a type of carbohydrate that the body can't digest. While most carbohydrates are broken down into sugar molecules, fiber passes through the body undigested. This unique trait allows fiber to play a crucial role in regulating the body's use of sugars, helping to keep hunger and blood sugar in check.

There are two types of fiber: soluble and insoluble. Soluble fiber dissolves in water to form a gel-like substance. It can help lower blood sugar levels by slowing down the absorption of sugar. It also lowers blood cholesterol levels by binding to cholesterol particles and removing them from the body. Foods rich in soluble fiber include oats, peas, beans, apples, citrus fruits, carrots, and barley.

Insoluble fiber, on the other hand, helps move material through your digestive system and increases stool bulk, beneficial for those who struggle with constipation or irregular stools. Whole-wheat flour, wheat bran, nuts, beans, and vegetables such as cauliflower, green beans, and potatoes are good sources of insoluble fiber.

For individuals managing Type 2 diabetes, incorporating a healthy amount of fiber into the diet can lead to significant benefits. It can improve blood sugar control, aid in weight loss by helping you feel fuller longer, and even reduce the risk of cardiovascular disease by lowering blood pressure and inflammation.

Whole foods are those that have been processed or refined as little as possible and are free from additives or other artificial substances. They are the opposite of processed foods, which often have sugar, unhealthy fats, and sodium added to make them taste better or extend their shelf life.

Emphasizing whole foods in your diet means more than just choosing brown rice over white rice or whole wheat bread over white bread. It's about making fruits, vegetables, whole grains, lean proteins, and healthy fats the cornerstone of your meals. These foods are rich in essential nutrients, including vitamins, minerals, fiber, and antioxidants, which can help protect against diabetes complications like heart disease and stroke.

Whole foods also have a lower glycemic index (GI) than processed foods. This means they cause a slower, more gradual rise in blood sugar levels, rather than the spikes associated with high-GI foods. Incorporating a variety of whole foods into your diet can help you maintain steady blood sugar levels, feel more satisfied, and provide your body with the nutrients it needs to function optimally.

Adopting a diet rich in fiber and whole foods doesn't have to be complicated. Here are some simple strategies to get started:

- **Start your day with whole grains.** Choose oatmeal, whole grain bread, or unsweetened whole grain cereals for breakfast.
- **Snack on fruits and vegetables.** Keep fresh, frozen, or dried fruits and vegetables on hand for an easy snack. Pair them with a handful of nuts for added protein and healthy fats.
- **Incorporate legumes into your meals.** Beans, lentils, and peas are excellent sources of soluble fiber and plant-based protein. Add them to soups, salads, or as a side dish.
- **Choose whole fruit over juice.** Whole fruits contain more fiber and less sugar than their juiced counterparts.
- **Select lean protein sources.** Incorporate lean meats, poultry, fish, tofu, and eggs into your meals for a balanced diet that includes insoluble fiber sources.

The benefits of a diet rich in fiber and whole foods extend beyond diabetes management. Such a diet can also improve digestive health, reduce the risk of certain cancers, and contribute to a

healthier heart. Furthermore, by focusing on whole foods, you're likely to consume fewer calories, less sugar, and less saturated fat, promoting weight loss and improved metabolic health.
Transitioning to a diet centered around fiber and whole foods is more than a dietary change; it's a lifestyle adjustment. It involves making conscious choices about what you eat, prioritizing the quality and nutritional value of food, and finding joy in the natural flavors and textures of whole foods.

Reading and Understanding Food Labels

The Nutrition Facts label is your guide to understanding what's in the food you're buying. Here's how to decipher the key components:

Serving Size: This is the foundation of the Nutrition Facts label. All the information on the label is based on this amount. Pay close attention to how many servings are in the package and compare it to how much you actually eat.

Calories: Provides the energy content of a serving. Managing calorie intake is crucial for weight management, an important aspect of diabetes care.

Carbohydrates: Since carbohydrates have the most direct impact on blood sugar levels, it's vital to pay attention to this section. Look not just at the total carbohydrates but also the breakdown: dietary fiber, sugars, and added sugars.

Dietary Fiber: Aim for foods high in fiber, as they can help control blood sugar levels.

Sugars: Includes both natural sugars from fruits, vegetables, and dairy, and added sugars. Limiting added sugars is key to managing diabetes.

Added Sugars: Recently added to labels, this number is crucial. The American Heart Association recommends limiting added sugars to no more than 6% of calories per day.

Protein: Essential for body repair and maintenance. It doesn't directly raise blood sugar levels, making it a key component of a balanced meal.

Fats: The label will list total fat, saturated fat, trans fat, and sometimes monounsaturated and polyunsaturated fats. While fats don't impact blood sugar levels as directly as carbohydrates, choosing healthy fats and limiting saturated and trans fats is important for heart health.

The ingredients list tells you exactly what's in the food, listed in order of quantity. Ingredients used in the greatest amount are listed first, followed in descending order by those in smaller amounts. This list can reveal the presence of added sugars, unhealthy fats, and artificial additives that you might want to avoid. Whole foods should be the first ingredients, indicating a healthier product.
One of the tricks to mastering food labels is learning to spot hidden sugars. They can appear under many names: sucrose, high-fructose corn syrup, barley malt, dextrose, maltose, and more.

Knowing these aliases can help you make better choices, especially since added sugars can significantly affect your blood sugar management.

Food packaging often includes health claims like "low fat," "high fiber," or "reduces cholesterol." While these can guide you towards healthier options, it's essential to read the Nutrition Facts label and ingredients list to ensure the product meets your dietary needs. Some products may be low in fat but high in added sugars, which could be detrimental to blood sugar control.

While understanding food labels is crucial, remember that the healthiest foods often don't come with labels. Fruits, vegetables, whole grains, lean proteins, and healthy fats are cornerstones of a diabetes-friendly diet and usually don't need ingredient lists or nutrition labels. Incorporating more whole foods into your diet can reduce the need to decode labels and ensure you're getting the nutrients you need without unwanted additives.

Practical Tips for Using Food Labels

Shop the perimeter of the grocery store first. This is where you'll find fresh produce, meats, and dairy products—foods that should make up the bulk of your diet.

When choosing packaged foods, opt for those with shorter ingredients lists. This often indicates fewer processed ingredients and additives.

Use the "5/20 rule." A food with 5% DV or less of a nutrient is considered low, while 20% DV or more is high. This can help you quickly assess if a food is a good source of nutrients like fiber or too high in elements like added sugars or saturated fat.

Be mindful of portion sizes. Adjust the numbers on the label based on how much you actually eat. If the serving size is one Cup and you eat two, remember to double the nutritional information.

Remember your dietary goals. Use the label to help you meet targets for carbohydrates, fiber, protein, and fat intake as part of your overall diabetes management plan.

PART II: RECIPE CHAPTERS

4. Breakfasts to Start Your Day Right

Energizing Smoothies and Juices

1. MORNING GLOW SMOOTHIE

P.T.: 5 min

C.T.: 0 min

M.C.: Blending

SERVINGS: 2

INGR.: 1 Cup spinach, fresh, 1/2 avocado, peeled and pitted, 1 banana, peeled, 1/2 Cup pineapple chunks, fresh or frozen, 1 Cup almond milk, unsweetened, 1 tsp flaxseed, ground, Ice cubes as needed

DIRECTIONS:

Place spinach, avocado, banana, pineapple chunks, almond milk, and ground flaxseed into a blender.

Add a handful of ice cubes to the blender if a colder smoothie is desired.

Blend on high speed until smooth and creamy.

Pour into glasses and serve immediately for a refreshing start to your day.

TIPS:

Add a scoop of your favorite protein powder for an extra protein boost.

If you prefer a sweeter smoothie, add a teaspoon of honey or maple syrup.

For extra hydration, replace half of the almond milk with coconut water.

N.V.: Calories: 190, Fat: 9g, Carbs: 27g, Protein: 4g, Sugar: 14g

2. BLUEBERRY OMEGA BOOST

P.T.: 5 min

C.T.: 0 min

M.C.: Blending

SERVINGS: 2

INGR.: 1 Cup blueberries, fresh or frozen, 1 banana, peeled, 1 Tbls chia seeds, 1 Tbls hemp seeds, 1 Cup Greek yogurt, plain, 1 Cup almond milk, unsweetened, Ice cubes as needed

DIRECTIONS:

Combine blueberries, banana, chia seeds, hemp seeds, Greek yogurt, and almond milk in a blender.

Add ice cubes according to preference for thickness and temperature.

Blend until smooth and creamy.

Serve the smoothie immediately, garnished with a few whole blueberries on top.

TIPS:

For a vegan version, use plant-based yogurt and a splash of maple syrup instead of Greek yogurt.

To thin the smoothie, add more almond milk until desired consistency is achieved.

Soak chia seeds in almond milk for 10 minutes before blending for a smoother texture.

N.V.: Calories: 210, Fat: 8g, Carbs: 29g, Protein: 12g, Sugar: 17g

3. GREEN DETOX JUICE

P.T.: 10 min

C.T.: 0 min

M.C.: Juicing

SERVINGS: 2

INGR.: 2 Cups kale, chopped, 1 green apple, cored and sliced, 1/2 cucumber, sliced, 1/2 lemon, peeled, 1 inch ginger, peeled, 1 Cup water

DIRECTIONS:

Wash all produce thoroughly under cold water.

Feed kale, green apple, cucumber, lemon, and ginger through the juicer.

Add water to the juicer to help extract all the juice.

Stir the juice well before pouring into glasses.

Serve the juice immediately, on an empty stomach for best detoxifying results.

TIPS:

For added sweetness, juice a carrot with the rest of the ingredients.

Drink this juice first thing in the morning to kickstart your digestive system.

If a juicer is not available, blend all ingredients with water and strain through a nut milk bag.

N.V.: Calories: 95, Fat: 0.5g, Carbs: 23g, Protein: 3g, Sugar: 12g

4. PROTEIN-PACKED CHOCOLATE ALMOND SMOOTHIE

P.T.: 5 min

C.T.: 0 min

M.C.: Blending

SERVINGS: 2

INGR.: 2 Tbls almond butter, 1 banana, peeled, 2 Tbls cocoa powder, unsweetened, 1 scoop chocolate protein powder, 1 Cup almond milk, unsweetened, Ice cubes as needed

DIRECTIONS:

Add almond butter, banana, cocoa powder, chocolate protein powder, and almond milk to a blender.

Toss in a few ice cubes for a chillier smoothie.

Blend on high until smooth and creamy.

Pour into glasses and enjoy as a nutritious breakfast or post-workout snack.

TIPS:

To increase the smoothie's fiber content, add a tablespoon of flaxseed meal or chia seeds.

Adjust the sweetness by adding a drizzle of honey or maple syrup if desired.

For a thicker smoothie, add more banana or use frozen banana slices.

N.V.: Calories: 280, Fat: 14g, Carbs: 25g, Protein: 20g, Sugar: 12g

Hearty Oatmeals and Porridges

1. COCONUT CHIA OATMEAL

P.T.: 5 min

C.T.: 15 min

M.C.: Simmering

SERVINGS: 2

INGR.: 1 Cup rolled oats, 1 Cup coconut milk, 1 Cup water, 2 Tblsp chia seeds, 1 Tblsp maple syrup, 1/2 tsp vanilla extract, Pinch of salt, Fresh berries and toasted coconut flakes for topping

DIRECTIONS:

In a medium saucepan, combine rolled oats, coconut milk, water, chia seeds, maple syrup, vanilla extract, and a pinch of salt. Stir to mix.

Bring to a simmer over medium heat, then reduce the heat to low. Cook, stirring occasionally, for about 15 minutes, or until the oats are tender and the mixture has thickened.

Remove from heat and let it stand for 2 minutes. The oatmeal will thicken further upon standing.

Serve in bowls, topped with fresh berries and toasted coconut flakes.

TIPS:

For a richer flavor, use full-fat coconut milk.

Add a tablespoon of almond butter or peanut butter for extra creaminess and protein.

The oatmeal can be stored in the refrigerator for up to 2 days. Reheat with a little extra milk to restore creaminess.

N.V.: Calories: 350, Fat: 18g, Carbs: 42g, Protein: 8g, Sugar: 10g

2. ALMOND BERRY PORRIDGE

P.T.: 5 min

C.T.: 10 min

M.C.: Simmering

SERVINGS: 2

INGR.: 1 Cup steel-cut oats, 2 Cups almond milk, 1/2 Cup mixed berries (fresh or frozen), 2 Tblsp almond slices, 1 Tblsp honey, 1/2 tsp cinnamon, Pinch of salt

DIRECTIONS:

In a medium saucepan, bring the almond milk to a boil. Add the steel-cut oats and a pinch of salt, then reduce the heat to a simmer.

Cook for about 10 minutes, stirring occasionally, until the oats are tender and the porridge has thickened.

Stir in the mixed berries, cinnamon, and honey. Cook for an additional 2 minutes, or until the berries are warm.

Serve the porridge in bowls, topped with almond slices.

TIPS:

For added sweetness and texture, top with a

dollop of Greek yogurt or a sprinkle of chia seeds before serving.

You can substitute almond milk with any plant-based milk of your choice.

If using frozen berries, there's no need to thaw them before adding to the porridge.

N.V.: Calories: 310, Fat: 9g, Carbs: 49g, Protein: 10g, Sugar: 12g

3. SAVORY MISO OATMEAL

P.T.: 5 min

C.T.: 15 min

M.C.: Simmering

SERVINGS: 2

INGR.: 1 Cup rolled oats, 2 1/2 Cups water, 1 Tblsp miso paste, 1/2 Cup diced tofu, 1/4 Cup sliced green onions, 1 tsp sesame seeds, 1 tsp soy sauce, 1/2 tsp grated ginger

DIRECTIONS:

In a medium saucepan, bring water to a boil. Stir in the rolled oats and reduce heat to a simmer.

Cook for about 10 minutes, stirring occasionally, until the oats are tender.

In a small bowl, dissolve the miso paste in a little hot water to make a smooth paste. Stir this miso paste into the oatmeal along with soy sauce and grated ginger.

Add the diced tofu and simmer for another 5 minutes.

Serve the oatmeal garnished with sliced green onions and sesame seeds.

TIPS:

For extra flavor, add a dash of sesame oil before serving.

Feel free to add other vegetables like spinach or kale for added nutrition.

Be sure not to boil the oatmeal after adding miso to preserve its probiotic benefits.

N.V.: Calories: 250, Fat: 6g, Carbs: 38g, Protein: 12g, Sugar: 2g

4. APPLE CINNAMON PROTEIN OATMEAL

P.T.: 5 min

C.T.: 10 min

M.C.: Simmering

SERVINGS: 2

INGR.: 1 Cup rolled oats, 2 Cups water, 1 medium apple, diced, 1 scoop vanilla protein powder, 1/2 tsp cinnamon, 2 Tblsp chopped walnuts, 1 Tblsp maple syrup, Pinch of salt

DIRECTIONS:

In a medium saucepan, bring the water to a boil. Add the rolled oats and a pinch of salt, then reduce the heat to a simmer.

Stir in the diced apple and cinnamon. Cook for about 10 minutes, stirring occasionally, until the oats are tender.

Remove from heat and stir in the vanilla protein powder until well combined.

Serve the oatmeal in bowls, drizzled with maple syrup and topped with chopped walnuts.

TIPS:

Ensure the oatmeal has cooled slightly before adding the protein powder to prevent it from denaturing.

Substitute the apple with pear for a different flavor profile.

For a creamier texture, you can replace half of the water with your choice of milk.

N.V.: Calories: 320, Fat: 8g, Carbs: 48g, Protein: 20g, Sugar: 15g

5. PUMPKIN SPICE PORRIDGE

P.T.: 5 min

C.T.: 15 min

M.C.: Simmering

SERVINGS: 2

INGR.: 1 Cup steel-cut oats, 2 Cups almond milk, 1/2 Cup pumpkin puree, 2 Tblsp pumpkin seeds, 1 tsp pumpkin pie spice, 2 Tblsp maple syrup, Pinch of salt

DIRECTIONS:

In a medium saucepan, bring the almond milk to a boil. Add the steel-cut oats and a pinch of salt, then reduce the heat to a simmer.

Cook for about 15 minutes, stirring occasionally, until the oats are tender.

Stir in the pumpkin puree, pumpkin pie spice, and maple syrup. Cook for an additional 2 minutes, or until everything is heated through.

Serve the porridge in bowls, topped with pumpkin seeds.

TIPS:

For an extra boost of protein, stir in a scoop of vanilla protein powder after cooking.

Top with a dollop of Greek yogurt for creaminess and a tangy contrast to the sweetness.

You can use homemade or canned pumpkin puree; just make sure it's unsweetened.

N.V.: Calories: 280, Fat: 7g, Carbs: 45g, Protein: 10g, Sugar: 12g

6. CHOCOLATE PEANUT BUTTER BANANA OATMEAL

P.T.: 5 min

C.T.: 10 min

M.C.: Simmering

SERVINGS: 2

INGR.: 1 Cup rolled oats, 2 Cups water, 1 banana, mashed, 2 Tblsp cocoa powder, unsweetened, 2 Tblsp peanut butter, 1 Tblsp honey, Pinch of salt

DIRECTIONS:

In a medium saucepan, bring the water to a boil. Add the rolled oats and a pinch of salt, then reduce the heat to a simmer.

Stir in the mashed banana and cocoa powder.

Cook for about 10 minutes, stirring occasionally, until the oats are tender.

Remove from heat and stir in the peanut

butter and honey until well combined.

Serve the oatmeal in bowls, with an extra dollop of peanut butter on top if desired.

TIPS:

For a richer oatmeal, you can substitute half of the water with milk of your choice.

Top with sliced banana or a sprinkle of chocolate chips for extra sweetness and texture.

To keep it vegan, use maple syrup instead of honey.

N.V.: Calories: 350, Fat: 14g, Carbs: 50g, Protein: 12g, Sugar: 18g

Protein-Packed Eggs and Breakfast Meats

1. SPINACH AND FETA OMELETTE

P.T.: 5 min

C.T.: 10 min

M.C.: Sautéing/Frying

SERVINGS: 2

INGR.: 4 eggs, beaten, 1 Cup spinach, fresh, 1/2 Cup feta cheese, crumbled, 1 Tblsp olive oil, Salt and pepper to taste

DIRECTIONS:

Heat olive oil in a non-stick frying pan over medium heat.

Add the spinach and sauté until wilted, about 2-3 minutes.

Pour the beaten eggs over the spinach. Season with salt and pepper. Cook for 2-3 minutes or until the eggs begin to set.

Sprinkle feta cheese over half of the omelette.

Fold the other half over the cheese.

Cook for another 2 minutes, then flip carefully and cook for 1-2 minutes more or until the eggs are fully set.

Serve hot, cut into portions.

TIPS:

Add diced tomatoes for a burst of flavor and color.

Ensure the pan is well-oiled to prevent sticking.

Use a lid to cover the omelette briefly to help melt the cheese and cook the top without flipping.

N.V.: Calories: 250, Fat: 18g, Carbs: 3g, Protein: 20g, Sugar: 2g

2. TURKEY BACON AND EGG MUFFINS

P.T.: 10 min

C.T.: 20 min

M.C.: Baking

SERVINGS: 6 muffins

INGR.: 6 slices turkey bacon, 6 eggs, 1/4 Cup shredded cheddar cheese, Salt and pepper to taste, Non-stick cooking spray

DIRECTIONS:

Preheat oven to 375°F (190°C). Spray a muffin tin with non-stick cooking spray.

Line each muffin Cup with a slice of turkey bacon, forming a Cup.

Crack an egg into each bacon-lined Cup. Season with salt and pepper.

Sprinkle shredded cheddar cheese on top of each egg.

Bake in the preheated oven for 15-20 minutes, or until the eggs are set to your liking.

Allow cooling for a couple of minutes before removing from the muffin tin. Serve warm.

TIPS:

Add finely chopped vegetables like bell peppers or spinach for extra nutrients.

For a crispy bacon shell, pre-cook the bacon slices for 2-3 minutes before lining the muffin Cups.

Let the muffins cool slightly before removing them from the tin to prevent breaking.

N.V.: Calories: 150, Fat: 10g, Carbs: 1g, Protein: 12g, Sugar: 0g

3. AVOCADO AND EGG BREAKFAST WRAP

P.T.: 5 min

C.T.: 5 min

M.C.: Sautéing

SERVINGS: 2 wraps

INGR.: 2 whole wheat tortillas, 4 eggs, beaten, 1 ripe avocado, sliced, 1/2 Cup spinach, fresh, 1/4 Cup salsa, 1 Tblsp olive oil, Salt and pepper to taste

DIRECTIONS:

Heat olive oil in a non-stick frying pan over medium heat. Pour in the beaten eggs, season with salt and pepper, and scramble until fully cooked.

Warm the tortillas in a separate pan or in the microwave for 10-15 seconds.

Divide the scrambled eggs between the tortillas, and top with avocado slices and fresh spinach.

Spoon salsa over the top of the fillings.

Roll up the tortillas tightly, folding in the sides as you go.

Serve immediately, with additional salsa on the side if desired.

TIPS:

For added flavor, incorporate a sprinkle of shredded cheese or a drizzle of hot sauce before rolling up the wraps.

To make this breakfast on-the-go friendly, wrap each in foil to keep them warm and contained.

Swap out the salsa for pesto for a different flavor profile.

N.V.: Calories: 320, Fat: 20g, Carbs: 22g, Protein: 15g, Sugar: 3g

4. SMOKED SALMON AND CREAM CHEESE SCRAMBLE

P.T.: 5 min

C.T.: 5 min

M.C.: Sautéing

SERVINGS: 2

INGR.: 4 eggs, beaten, 2 oz smoked salmon, chopped, 2 Tblsp cream cheese, 1 Tblsp chives, chopped, 1 Tblsp olive oil, Salt and pepper to taste

DIRECTIONS:

Heat olive oil in a non-stick frying pan over medium heat.

Pour the beaten eggs into the pan. As they begin to set, gently stir in the cream cheese and smoked salmon.

Continue to cook, gently folding the eggs until they are softly scrambled.

Season with salt and pepper, and sprinkle with chopped chives.

Serve immediately on toasted whole-grain bread if desired.

TIPS:

Avoid overcooking the eggs to keep the scramble soft and creamy.

For a lighter version, use light cream cheese or a dollop of Greek yogurt instead.

Garnish with additional fresh herbs like dill or parsley for enhanced flavor.

N.V.: Calories: 290, Fat: 22g, Carbs: 2g, Protein: 20g, Sugar: 1g

5. CHICKEN SAUSAGE AND VEGETABLE SKILLET

P.T.: 10 min

C.T.: 15 min

M.C.: Sautéing

SERVINGS: 4

INGR.: 4 chicken sausages, sliced, 1 Cup bell peppers, diced, 1 Cup onions, diced, 2 Cups spinach, fresh, 1 Tblsp olive oil, Salt and pepper to taste

DIRECTIONS:

Heat olive oil in a large skillet over medium heat. Add the sliced chicken sausages and cook until browned, about 5 minutes.

Add the diced bell peppers and onions to the skillet. Sauté until the vegetables are soft, about 5 minutes.

Stir in the spinach and cook until wilted, about 2 minutes. Season with salt and pepper.

Serve hot, with optional whole-grain toast or eggs cooked to your preference on the side.

TIPS:

Use a variety of colored bell peppers for a vibrant dish.

For added spice, choose spicy chicken sausage or add red pepper flakes while cooking.

This skillet can be easily adapted for breakfast, lunch, or dinner.

N.V.: Calories: 250, Fat: 15g, Carbs: 10g, Protein: 18g, Sugar: 3g

5. Nourishing Lunches

Quick and Easy Salads

1. SUMMER BERRY SPINACH SALAD

P.T.: 10 min

C.T.: 0 min

M.C.: Mixing

SERVINGS: 4

INGR.: 4 Cups spinach, fresh, 1 Cup strawberries, sliced, 1/2 Cup blueberries, 1/4 Cup feta cheese, crumbled, 1/4 Cup walnuts, chopped, For the dressing: 3 Tblsp olive oil, 2 Tblsp balsamic vinegar, 1 tsp honey, Salt and pepper to taste

DIRECTIONS:

In a large salad bowl, combine spinach, strawberries, blueberries, feta cheese, and chopped walnuts.

In a small bowl, whisk together olive oil, balsamic vinegar, honey, salt, and pepper to create the dressing.

Drizzle the dressing over the salad and toss gently to coat.

Serve immediately, enjoying the fresh, summery flavors.

TIPS:

To make the salad a complete meal, add grilled chicken or salmon.

For a nut-free version, substitute sunflower seeds for the walnuts.

The salad dressing can be made in advance and stored in the refrigerator for up to a week.

N.V.: Calories: 200, Fat: 15g, Carbs: 14g, Protein: 5g, Sugar: 9g

2. CRISP CUCUMBER AND RADISH SALAD

P.T.: 10 min

C.T.: 0 min

M.C.: Mixing

SERVINGS: 4

INGR.: 2 cucumbers, thinly sliced, 10 radishes, thinly sliced, 1/4 Cup red onion, thinly sliced, 2 Tblsp dill, fresh, chopped, For the dressing: 3 Tblsp apple cider vinegar, 1 Tblsp olive oil, 1 tsp honey, Salt and pepper to taste

DIRECTIONS:

In a large mixing bowl, combine the sliced cucumbers, radishes, red onion, and dill.

In a small bowl, whisk together apple cider vinegar, olive oil, honey, salt, and pepper to make the dressing.

Pour the dressing over the vegetables and toss to coat evenly.

Chill in the refrigerator for 15 minutes before serving to allow flavors to meld.

TIPS:

This salad is a refreshing side dish for barbecue or grilled meats.

For added crunch, sprinkle with toasted sesame seeds just before serving.

The salad can be prepared a few hours in advance, making it perfect for gatherings.

N.V.: Calories: 80, Fat: 7g, Carbs: 4g, Protein: 1g, Sugar: 3g

3. AVOCADO AND BLACK BEAN SALAD

P.T.: 15 min

C.T.: 0 min

M.C.: Mixing

SERVINGS: 4

INGR.: 1 can (15 oz.) black beans, rinsed and drained, 2 avocados, diced, 1 Cup corn, fresh or frozen (thawed), 1/2 Cup cherry tomatoes, halved, 1/4 Cup cilantro, chopped, 1 lime, juiced, 2 Tblsp olive oil, Salt and pepper to taste

DIRECTIONS:

In a large salad bowl, combine black beans, diced avocados, corn, cherry tomatoes, and chopped cilantro.

Drizzle with lime juice and olive oil. Season with salt and pepper to taste.

Toss gently to mix all the ingredients well.

Serve immediately or chill for about 30 minutes before serving for enhanced flavors.

TIPS:

To prevent the avocado from browning, add the lime juice directly to the diced avocado before adding to the salad.

For a spicy kick, add diced jalapeño or a pinch of cayenne pepper to the salad.

This salad pairs beautifully with grilled meats or can be enjoyed as a hearty standalone dish.

N.V.: Calories: 250, Fat: 15g, Carbs: 27g, Protein: 7g, Sugar: 2g

WARM AND COMFORTING SOUPS

1. TUSCAN WHITE BEAN SOUP

P.T.: 10 min

C.T.: 30 min

M.C.: Simmering

SERVINGS: 4

INGR.: 1 Tblsp olive oil, 1 onion finely chopped, 2 garlic cloves minced, 1 carrot diced, 1 stalk celery diced, 4 Cups vegetable broth, 1 can (15 oz.) cannellini beans rinsed and drained, 1 tsp dried thyme, 1 bay leaf, 2 Cups kale roughly chopped, Salt and pepper to taste, Grated Parmesan cheese for serving

DIRECTIONS:

Heat olive oil in a large pot over medium heat. Add onion, garlic, carrot, and celery, cooking until softened, about 5 minutes.

Stir in vegetable broth, cannellini beans, thyme, and bay leaf. Bring to a boil, then reduce heat to low and simmer for 20 minutes.

Add kale, season with salt and pepper, and cook until the kale is wilted, about 5 minutes.

Remove the bay leaf, serve the soup into bowls, and top with grated Parmesan cheese.

TIPS:

For a thicker soup, mash some of the beans

before adding them to the pot.

The soup can be made in advance and tastes even better the next day.

Serve with crusty bread for dipping.

N.V.: Calories: 190, Fat: 4g, Carbs: 30g, Protein: 10g, Sugar: 4g

2. CLASSIC CHICKEN NOODLE SOUP

P.T.: 15 min

C.T.: 40 min

M.C.: Boiling

SERVINGS: 4

INGR.: 1 Tblsp olive oil, 1 lb. chicken breast, 1 onion chopped, 2 carrots sliced, 2 celery stalks sliced, 6 Cups chicken broth, 2 tsp dried parsley, 1 tsp dried thyme, 6 oz. egg noodles, Salt and pepper to taste

DIRECTIONS:

In a large pot, heat olive oil over medium heat. Add the chicken breast and cook until browned on both sides. Remove chicken and set aside.

In the same pot, add onion, carrots, and celery, cooking until the vegetables start to soften.

Pour in chicken broth, add parsley, thyme, and the cooked chicken breast. Bring to a boil, then reduce heat and simmer for 20 minutes.

Remove chicken, shred it, and return it to the pot. Add egg noodles and cook until tender, about 10 minutes. Season with salt and pepper.

Serve hot, with fresh parsley for garnish if desired.

TIPS:

Use homemade chicken broth for richer flavor.

For a gluten-free version, substitute egg noodles with rice or gluten-free pasta.

Add a squeeze of lemon juice before serving for added brightness.

N.V.: Calories: 330, Fat: 7g, Carbs: 40g, Protein: 28g, Sugar: 3g

3. ROASTED BUTTERNUT SQUASH SOUP

P.T.: 20 min

C.T.: 1 hr

M.C.: Roasting and Blending

SERVINGS: 4

INGR.: 1 large butternut squash peeled and cubed, 3 Tblsp olive oil divided, 1 onion diced, 3 garlic cloves minced, 4 Cups vegetable broth, 1/2 tsp cinnamon, 1/4 tsp nutmeg, Salt and pepper to taste, Cream for serving

DIRECTIONS:

Preheat oven to 400°F (200°C). Toss butternut squash with 2 tablespoons of olive oil, salt, and pepper. Spread on a baking sheet and roast until tender and caramelized, about 30 minutes.

In a pot, heat the remaining olive oil over medium heat. Add onion and garlic, cooking until soft.

Add roasted squash, vegetable broth, cinnamon, and nutmeg. Bring to a simmer and cook for 20 minutes.

Blend the soup until smooth, using an immersion blender. Season with salt and pepper.

Serve hot, drizzled with cream.

TIPS:

For a vegan version, use coconut milk instead of cream.

Garnish with roasted pumpkin seeds for added texture.

Soup can be frozen for up to 3 months.

N.V.: Calories: 250, Fat: 14g, Carbs: 33g, Protein: 3g, Sugar: 7g

4. SPICY LENTIL AND TOMATO SOUP

P.T.: 10 min

C.T.: 25 min

M.C.: Simmering

SERVINGS: 4

INGR.: 1 Tblsp olive oil, 1 onion finely chopped, 2 garlic cloves minced, 1 carrot diced, 1 stalk celery diced, 1 tsp ground cumin, 1/2 tsp chili flakes, 1 Cup red lentils, 4 Cups vegetable broth, 1 can (14 oz.) diced tomatoes, Salt and pepper to taste, Fresh cilantro for garnish

DIRECTIONS:

Heat olive oil in a large pot over medium heat. Add onion and garlic, cooking until soft.

Stir in carrot, celery, cumin, and chili flakes, cooking for another 2 minutes.

Add red lentils, vegetable broth, and diced tomatoes. Season with salt and pepper.

Bring to a boil, then reduce heat and simmer for 20 minutes, or until lentils are tender.

Serve the soup garnished with fresh cilantro.

TIPS:

For a creamier texture, blend half the soup and then combine it with the remaining half.

Add a squeeze of lemon juice before serving for extra zest.

Serve with warm naan or crusty bread.

N.V.: Calories: 210, Fat: 4g, Carbs: 34g, Protein: 11g, Sugar: 6g

5. BROCCOLI AND CHEDDAR SOUP

P.T.: 10 min

C.T.: 20 min

M.C.: Simmering

SERVINGS: 4

INGR.: 2 Tblsp unsalted butter, 1 small onion chopped, 1/4 Cup all-purpose flour, 2 Cups chicken or vegetable broth, 2 Cups milk, 4 Cups broccoli florets, 1 carrot julienned, 1/4 tsp nutmeg, 1 Cup sharp cheddar cheese grated, Salt and pepper to taste

DIRECTIONS:

In a large pot, melt butter over medium heat. Add onion and cook until softened.

Stir in flour to create a roux, cooking for 1-2 minutes. Gradually whisk in broth and milk, avoiding lumps.

Add broccoli, carrot, and nutmeg. Bring to a boil, then reduce heat and simmer until vegetables are tender, about 10-15 minutes.

Stir in cheddar cheese until melted. Season with salt and pepper.

Serve hot, with extra cheese on top if desired.

TIPS:

For a smoother soup, use an immersion blender to puree it to your desired consistency.

Substitute with low-fat milk and cheese for a lighter version.

A dash of hot sauce adds a nice kick to the soup.

N.V.: Calories: 280, Fat: 16g, Carbs: 18g, Protein: 15g, Sugar: 7g

6. SWEET POTATO AND GINGER SOUP

P.T.: 15 min

C.T.: 30 min

M.C.: Simmering

SERVINGS: 4

INGR.: 2 Tblsp olive oil, 1 onion chopped, 2 cloves garlic minced, 1 Tblsp fresh ginger grated, 2 large sweet potatoes peeled and cubed, 4 Cups vegetable broth, 1 can (14 oz.) coconut milk, Salt and pepper to taste, Pumpkin seeds for garnish

DIRECTIONS:

In a large pot, heat olive oil over medium heat. Add onion, garlic, and ginger, cooking until the onion is translucent.

Add sweet potatoes and vegetable broth. Season with salt and pepper.

Bring to a boil, then reduce heat and simmer until sweet potatoes are soft, about 20 minutes.

Stir in coconut milk and cook for another 5 minutes.

Blend the soup until smooth using an immersion blender.

Serve hot, garnished with pumpkin seeds.

TIPS:

Add a pinch of cayenne pepper for a spicy twist.

Roast the sweet potatoes beforehand to deepen the flavor.

Coconut cream can be used for a thicker, richer soup.

N.V.: Calories: 300, Fat: 18g, Carbs: 32g, Protein: 4g, Sugar: 7g

1. GRILLED VEGETABLE AND HUMMUS WRAP

P.T.: 15 min

C.T.: 10 min

M.C.: Grilling

SERVINGS: 4

INGR.: 2 zucchinis, sliced lengthwise, 1 red bell pepper, sliced, 1 yellow bell pepper, sliced, 1 eggplant, sliced lengthwise, 1 Tblsp olive oil, Salt and pepper to taste, 4 whole wheat wraps, 1 Cup hummus, 1 Cup baby spinach leaves

DIRECTIONS:

Preheat grill to medium-high heat. Toss zucchini, bell peppers, and eggplant with olive oil, salt, and pepper.

Grill vegetables until tender and charred, about 5 minutes per side.

Spread each wrap with a generous layer of hummus. Top with grilled vegetables and baby spinach.

Roll up the wraps tightly, slice in half, and serve.

TIPS:

For added flavor, sprinkle the vegetables with balsamic vinegar before grilling.

Any leftover grilled vegetables can be stored and used for salads or other wraps.

To make this recipe gluten-free, use gluten-free wraps instead of whole wheat.

N.V.: Calories: 320, Fat: 12g, Carbs: 45g, Protein: 12g, Sugar: 8g

2. TURKEY AND AVOCADO CLUB SANDWICH

P.T.: 10 min

C.T.: 0 min

M.C.: Assembling

SERVINGS: 4

INGR.: 8 slices whole grain bread, toasted, 1 lb. sliced turkey breast, 1 avocado, sliced, 8 slices tomato, 4 lettuce leaves, 4 Tblsp mayonnaise, 8 slices cooked bacon, Salt and pepper to taste

DIRECTIONS:

Spread mayonnaise on one side of each slice of toasted bread.

On four slices of bread, layer sliced turkey, bacon, avocado, tomato, and lettuce. Season with salt and pepper.

Top with the remaining slices of bread, mayonnaise side down.

Cut each sandwich in half and serve immediately.

TIPS:

To reduce calories, use a low-fat mayonnaise or substitute with mustard.

Add a slice of cheese for extra flavor, if desired.

For a healthier version, use turkey bacon instead of regular bacon.

N.V.: Calories: 450, Fat: 20g, Carbs: 38g, Protein: 35g, Sugar: 5g

3. CHICKPEA SALAD SANDWICH

P.T.: 15 min

C.T.: 0 min

M.C.: Mashing/Mixing

SERVINGS: 4

INGR.: 1 can (15 oz.) chickpeas, rinsed and drained, 1/4 Cup celery, finely chopped, 1/4 Cup red onion, finely chopped, 1/4 Cup mayonnaise, 1 Tblsp mustard, 1 tsp lemon juice, Salt and pepper to taste, 8 slices whole grain bread, Lettuce leaves

DIRECTIONS:

In a bowl, mash the chickpeas with a fork or potato masher until coarsely mashed.

Add celery, red onion, mayonnaise, mustard, and lemon juice to the mashed chickpeas. Season with salt and pepper and stir to combine.

Spread the chickpea salad on four slices of bread. Top with lettuce leaves.

Cover with the remaining slices of bread, cut each sandwich in half, and serve.

TIPS:

For a vegan version, use vegan mayonnaise and mustard.

Add diced pickles or capers for extra tanginess.

The chickpea salad can be made in advance and stored in the refrigerator for up to 3 days.

N.V.: Calories: 350, Fat: 12g, Carbs: 48g, Protein: 14g, Sugar: 7g

4. SPICY TUNA WRAP

P.T.: 10 min

C.T.: 0 min

M.C.: Mixing

SERVINGS: 4

INGR.: 2 cans (5 oz. each) tuna in water, drained, 1/4 Cup mayonnaise, 2 Tblsp sriracha sauce, 1/4 Cup cucumber, diced, 1/4 Cup carrot, shredded, 4 whole wheat wraps, 1 avocado, sliced, 1 Cup mixed greens

DIRECTIONS:

In a bowl, mix the drained tuna with mayonnaise and sriracha sauce until well combined.

Stir in diced cucumber and shredded carrot.

Lay out the whole wheat wraps and evenly distribute the tuna mixture among them.

Add slices of avocado and a handful of mixed greens on top of the tuna.

Roll up the wraps tightly, slice in half, and serve immediately.

TIPS:

Adjust the amount of sriracha sauce according to your spice preference.

For added crunch, include thinly sliced bell peppers.

If whole wheat wraps aren't available, use any large leafy green as a wrap alternative for a low-carb option.

N.V.: Calories: 350, Fat: 15g, Carbs: 35g, Protein: 20g, Sugar: 3g

5. ROASTED VEGETABLE AND GOAT CHEESE PANINI

P.T.: 15 min

C.T.: 10 min

M.C.: Grilling

SERVINGS: 4

INGR.: 1 zucchini, sliced, 1 red bell pepper, sliced, 1 yellow bell pepper, sliced, 1 eggplant, sliced, 2 Tblsp olive oil, Salt and pepper to taste, 8 slices sourdough bread, 4 oz. goat cheese, softened, 1/4 Cup pesto sauce

DIRECTIONS:

Preheat a grill pan over medium heat. Toss zucchini, bell peppers, and eggplant with olive oil, salt, and pepper.

Grill the vegetables until tender and charred, about 3-5 minutes per side.

Spread goat cheese on four slices of sourdough bread. Spread pesto on the other four slices.

Assemble the sandwiches by layering the grilled vegetables between the slices of bread with goat cheese and pesto.

Grill the sandwiches in the grill pan, pressing them down with a spatula, until golden brown on both sides.

TIPS:

For extra flavor, add a few fresh basil leaves inside the sandwiches.

If you don't have a grill pan, a regular skillet works fine, or use a panini press.

Serve with a side of mixed greens for a complete meal.

N.V.: Calories: 420, Fat: 22g, Carbs: 45g, Protein: 15g, Sugar: 8g

6. CHICKEN CAESAR SALAD WRAP

P.T.: 10 min

C.T.: 0 min

M.C.: Assembling

SERVINGS: 4

INGR.: 2 Cups cooked chicken, shredded, 1/2 Cup Caesar dressing, 2 Cups romaine lettuce, chopped, 1/4 Cup Parmesan cheese, grated, 1/2 Cup croutons, lightly crushed, 4 whole wheat tortillas

DIRECTIONS:

In a bowl, combine shredded chicken with Caesar dressing until the chicken is evenly coated.

Add chopped romaine lettuce and grated Parmesan cheese to the chicken mixture. Gently mix.

Sprinkle the crushed croutons over the mixture.

Divide the chicken Caesar salad among the whole wheat tortillas, placing the mixture down the center of each tortilla.

Roll up the tortillas tightly, folding in the edges to enclose the filling. Slice in half and serve immediately.

TIPS:

To make this wrap healthier, use a light Caesar dressing or Greek yogurt-based dressing.

Add slices of avocado for creaminess and extra nutrients.

For a gluten-free option, use gluten-free tortillas.

N.V.: Calories: 380, Fat: 18g, Carbs: 30g, Protein: 25g, Sugar: 3g

6. Satisfying Dinners

Vegetable-Forward Dishes

1. ROASTED CAULIFLOWER STEAKS WITH TAHINI SAUCE

P.T.: 10 min

C.T.: 25 min

M.C.: Roasting

SERVINGS: 4

INGR.: 2 large heads cauliflower, 2 Tblsp olive oil, Salt and pepper to taste, For the tahini sauce: 1/4 Cup tahini, 2 Tblsp lemon juice, 1 garlic clove minced, 2-4 Tblsp water, Salt to taste, For garnish: 2 Tblsp chopped parsley, 1 Tblsp sesame seeds

DIRECTIONS:

Preheat oven to 400°F (200°C). Slice cauliflower heads into 1-inch thick steaks, keeping the core intact.

Place cauliflower steaks on a baking sheet. Brush both sides with olive oil and season with salt and pepper.

Roast in the preheated oven for about 25 minutes, flipping halfway through, until golden and tender.

For the tahini sauce, whisk together tahini, lemon juice, garlic, and water until smooth. Season with salt.

Serve cauliflower steaks drizzled with tahini sauce and garnished with parsley and sesame seeds.

TIPS:

If the cauliflower steaks break while slicing, roast the florets following the same method.

The tahini sauce can be adjusted with more water for a pourable consistency.

Serve with quinoa or couscous for a complete meal.

N.V.: Calories: 210, Fat: 14g, Carbs: 18g, Protein: 6g, Sugar: 5g

2. ZUCCHINI NOODLES WITH AVOCADO PESTO

P.T.: 15 min

C.T.: 0 min

M.C.: Spiralizing/Mixing

SERVINGS: 4

INGR.: 4 large zucchinis, 1 ripe avocado, 1/2 Cup fresh basil leaves, 1/4 Cup pine nuts, 2 garlic cloves, 2 Tblsp lemon juice, Salt and pepper to taste, 1/4 Cup grated Parmesan cheese (optional)

DIRECTIONS:

Use a spiralizer to turn zucchinis into noodles. Place in a large bowl.

In a food processor, blend avocado, basil, pine nuts, garlic, and lemon juice until smooth. Season with salt and pepper.

Toss zucchini noodles with avocado pesto until well coated.

Serve immediately, sprinkled with Parmesan cheese if using.

TIPS:

For a non-vegan option, add grilled chicken or shrimp on top.

Squeeze additional lemon juice on top before serving for extra zing.

If not serving immediately, store the pesto and zucchini noodles separately in the fridge to prevent sogginess.

N.V.: Calories: 220, Fat: 16g, Carbs: 16g, Protein: 6g, Sugar: 5g

3. SWEET POTATO AND BLACK BEAN BOWL

P.T.: 10 min

C.T.: 30 min

M.C.: Roasting/Boiling

SERVINGS: 4

INGR.: 2 large sweet potatoes cubed, 1 Tblsp olive oil, 1 tsp smoked paprika, Salt and pepper to taste, 1 can (15 oz.) black beans rinsed and drained, 2 Cups cooked quinoa, 1 avocado sliced, For the dressing: 2 Tblsp lime juice, 1 Tblsp olive oil, 1 tsp honey, 1/4 tsp cumin, Salt to taste

DIRECTIONS:

Preheat oven to 425°F (220°C). Toss sweet potatoes with olive oil, smoked paprika, salt, and pepper. Roast for 25-30 minutes until tender.

Prepare quinoa according to package instructions.

Whisk together lime juice, olive oil, honey, cumin, and salt for the dressing.

Assemble bowls with quinoa, roasted sweet potatoes, black beans, and avocado slices. Drizzle with dressing.

TIPS:

Add fresh cilantro or green onions for a fresh flavor boost.

Include a dollop of Greek yogurt for creaminess.

Can be served warm or cold, making it perfect for meal prep.

N.V.: Calories: 420, Fat: 15g, Carbs: 64g, Protein: 12g, Sugar: 9g

LEAN MEATS AND SEAFOOD

1. HERB-CRUSTED SALMON

P.T.: 10 min

C.T.: 15 min

M.C.: Baking

SERVINGS: 4

INGR.: 4 salmon fillets (6 oz. each), 2 Tblsp olive oil, 1 Tblsp Dijon mustard, 1/2 Cup panko breadcrumbs, 1 Tblsp fresh dill, chopped, 1 Tblsp fresh parsley, chopped, Salt and pepper to taste, Lemon wedges for serving

DIRECTIONS:

Preheat the oven to 400°F (200°C). Line a baking sheet with parchment paper.

Brush each salmon fillet with olive oil and Dijon mustard.

In a bowl, mix panko breadcrumbs with dill, parsley, salt, and pepper. Press the breadcrumb mixture onto the mustard-coated side of each fillet.

Place fillets breadcrumb side up on the prepared baking sheet. Bake for 15 minutes, or until the crust is golden and the salmon is cooked through.

Serve immediately with lemon wedges on the side.

TIPS:

Ensure the salmon is at room temperature before baking for even cooking.

For a gluten-free option, use gluten-free breadcrumbs or almond meal.

The herb crust can be prepared in advance and stored in the refrigerator.

N.V.: Calories: 295, Fat: 15g, Carbs: 9g, Protein: 31g, Sugar: 0g

2. LEMON GARLIC CHICKEN BREASTS

P.T.: 15 min (plus marinating time)

C.T.: 20 min

M.C.: Grilling

SERVINGS: 4

INGR.: 4 chicken breasts (boneless, skinless), 1/4 Cup olive oil, 1/4 Cup lemon juice, 4 garlic cloves, minced, 1 tsp dried oregano, Salt and pepper to taste

DIRECTIONS:

In a bowl, whisk together olive oil, lemon juice, garlic, oregano, salt, and pepper. Pour over chicken breasts in a zip-lock bag. Marinate in the refrigerator for at least 1 hour, preferably overnight.

Preheat grill to medium-high heat. Remove chicken from marinade, discarding any excess marinade.

Grill chicken for 10 minutes on each side, or until cooked through and internal temperature reaches 165°F (74°C).

Let the chicken rest for 5 minutes before slicing. Serve with a side of grilled vegetables or salad.

TIPS:

For added flavor, zest the lemon before juicing and add the zest to the marinade.

Pound the chicken breasts to an even thickness for uniform cooking.

A meat thermometer is helpful for ensuring the chicken is perfectly cooked.

N.V.: Calories: 265, Fat: 14g, Carbs: 3g, Protein: 31g, Sugar: 0g

3. SPICED TURKEY MEATBALLS

P.T.: 20 min

C.T.: 25 min

M.C.: Baking

SERVINGS: 4

INGR.: 1 lb ground turkey, 1 egg, beaten, 1/4 Cup breadcrumbs, 2 Tblsp fresh cilantro, chopped, 1 tsp cumin, 1/2 tsp smoked paprika, Salt and pepper to taste, 1/4 Cup yogurt, for serving

DIRECTIONS:

Preheat the oven to 375°F (190°C). Line a baking tray with parchment paper.

In a bowl, combine ground turkey, egg, breadcrumbs, cilantro, cumin, smoked paprika, salt, and pepper. Mix until well combined.

Form the mixture into small meatballs and place on the prepared baking tray.

Bake for 25 minutes, or until meatballs are cooked through.

Serve the meatballs with a dollop of yogurt on the side.

TIPS:

Soak the breadcrumbs in a little milk for 5 minutes before mixing for moister meatballs.

The meatballs can be made in advance and frozen for a quick dinner option.

Serve with a cucumber and tomato salad for a refreshing side.

N.V.: Calories: 220, Fat: 11g, Carbs: 6g, Protein: 24g, Sugar: 2g

CREATIVE PASTA AND RICE ALTERNATIVES

1. CAULIFLOWER RICE STIR-FRY

P.T.: 10 min

C.T.: 15 min

M.C.: Sautéing

SERVINGS: 4

INGR.: 1 head cauliflower, grated into rice-sized pieces, 2 Tblsp sesame oil, 1 small onion, diced, 2 garlic cloves, minced, 1 Cup mixed vegetables (carrots, peas, bell peppers), diced, 2 eggs, lightly beaten, 3 Tblsp soy sauce, 1 Tblsp green onions, chopped, Salt and pepper to taste

DIRECTIONS:

Heat sesame oil in a large skillet over medium heat. Sauté onion and garlic until soft.

Add the mixed vegetables and cook until tender.

Stir in the grated cauliflower and cook for an additional 5 minutes.

Push the cauliflower mixture to the side of the skillet, pour in the beaten eggs, and scramble until fully cooked.

Mix the scrambled eggs with the cauliflower rice. Stir in soy sauce and season with salt and pepper.

Garnish with green onions before serving.

TIPS:

For added protein, include diced chicken or shrimp.

Enhance the flavor with a drizzle of sesame oil before serving.

Cauliflower rice can be prepared in advance and stored in the refrigerator.

N.V.: Calories: 150, Fat: 8g, Carbs: 12g, Protein: 8g, Sugar: 4g

2. ZUCCHINI NOODLE PESTO

P.T.: 15 min

C.T.: 0 min

M.C.: Spiralizing/Mixing

SERVINGS: 4

INGR.: 4 large zucchinis, spiralized into noodles, 1 Cup fresh basil leaves, 1/3 Cup pine nuts, 2 garlic cloves, 1/2 Cup grated Parmesan cheese, 1/2 Cup olive oil, Salt and pepper to taste, Cherry tomatoes for garnish

DIRECTIONS:

Place basil leaves, pine nuts, garlic, Parmesan cheese, and olive oil in a food processor. Blend until smooth to make the pesto. Season with salt and pepper.

In a large bowl, toss the zucchini noodles with the pesto until well coated.

Serve topped with cherry tomatoes and additional Parmesan cheese if desired.

TIPS:

For a creamy pesto, add a tablespoon of cream or Greek yogurt.

Zucchini noodles can be lightly sautéed for 2-3 minutes if preferred warm.

Substitute pine nuts with walnuts for a different flavor.

N.V.: Calories: 310, Fat: 27g, Carbs: 8g, Protein: 8g, Sugar: 4g

3. BUTTERNUT SQUASH LASAGNA

P.T.: 20 min

C.T.: 45 min

M.C.: Baking

SERVINGS: 6

INGR.: 1 large butternut squash, peeled and sliced thin, 2 Cups ricotta cheese, 1 egg, 2 Cups spinach, cooked and squeezed dry, 1/2 Cup grated Parmesan cheese, 2 Cups mozzarella cheese, shredded, 2 Cups marinara sauce, Salt and pepper to taste

DIRECTIONS:

Preheat the oven to 375°F (190°C).

In a bowl, mix ricotta cheese, egg, spinach, Parmesan cheese, salt, and pepper.

In a baking dish, layer marinara sauce, butternut squash slices, ricotta mixture, and mozzarella cheese. Repeat layers.

Cover with foil and bake for 40 minutes. Remove foil and bake for an additional 5 minutes or until cheese is bubbly and golden.

Let it cool for 10 minutes before serving.

TIPS:

For a meat version, layer cooked ground turkey or beef between the squash slices.

Ensure the butternut squash is sliced thinly for quicker cooking.

Let the lasagna set before slicing to ensure it holds its shape.

N.V.: Calories: 350, Fat: 18g, Carbs: 28g, Protein: 22g, Sugar: 8g

4. SPAGHETTI SQUASH PAD THAI

P.T.: 20 min

C.T.: 40 min

M.C.: Baking and Sautéing

SERVINGS: 4

INGR.: 1 large spaghetti squash, halved and seeds removed, 1 Tblsp olive oil, 2 chicken breasts, thinly sliced, 2 cloves garlic, minced, 1 red bell pepper, thinly sliced, 1 carrot, julienned, 2 green onions, chopped, 1/4 Cup peanuts, chopped, For the sauce: 2 Tblsp tamarind paste, 2 Tblsp fish sauce, 1 Tblsp soy sauce, 2 Tblsp brown sugar, 1/2 Cup water, 1 lime, juiced

DIRECTIONS:

Preheat the oven to 400°F (200°C). Place the spaghetti squash halves cut-side down on a baking sheet and roast until tender, about 30-40 minutes.

In a small bowl, whisk together tamarind paste, fish sauce, soy sauce, brown sugar, water, and lime juice to make the sauce. Set aside.

Heat olive oil in a large skillet over medium heat. Add chicken and garlic, sautéing until the chicken is cooked through.

Add the red bell pepper and carrot to the skillet, cooking until slightly softened.

Once the spaghetti squash is cooked, use a fork to scrape the insides into strands. Add the spaghetti squash strands to the skillet.

Pour the sauce over the spaghetti squash mixture, tossing to combine. Cook for an additional 2-3 minutes to heat through.

Serve garnished with green onions and chopped peanuts.

TIPS:

For a vegetarian option, omit the chicken and add more vegetables or tofu.

Adjust the heat by adding chili flakes or sriracha to the sauce if desired.

Be careful not to overcook the spaghetti squash to avoid mushy noodles.

N.V.: Calories: 320, Fat: 10g, Carbs: 34g, Protein: 26g, Sugar: 14g

5. BROCCOLI RICE CASSEROLE

P.T.: 15 min

C.T.: 30 min

M.C.: Baking

SERVINGS: 6

INGR.: 1 head of broccoli, cut into florets and pulsed in a food processor until rice-like, 1 Tblsp olive oil, 1 onion, diced, 2 cloves garlic, minced, 1 Cup mushrooms, sliced, 2 Cups cooked chicken, shredded, 1 Cup Greek yogurt, 1/2 Cup chicken broth, 1 Cup cheddar cheese, shredded, Salt and pepper to taste

DIRECTIONS:

Preheat the oven to 375°F (190°C). Grease a baking dish with olive oil.

Heat olive oil in a skillet over medium heat. Add onion, garlic, and mushrooms, cooking until softened.

In a large bowl, combine the broccoli rice, sautéed vegetables, shredded chicken, Greek yogurt, and chicken broth. Season with salt and pepper.

Transfer the mixture to the prepared baking dish. Top with shredded cheddar cheese.

Bake for 25-30 minutes, or until the cheese is bubbly and golden.

Serve hot, directly from the oven.

TIPS:

Customize the casserole by adding other vegetables like bell peppers or zucchini.

For a crunchy topping, add a mixture of

breadcrumbs and parmesan cheese before baking.
Ensure the broccoli rice is dry to prevent the casserole from becoming soggy.

N.V.: Calories: 270, Fat: 15g, Carbs: 12g, Protein: 25g, Sugar: 3g

7. SNACKS AND SIDES

HEALTHY SNACK IDEAS

1. CRISPY CHICKPEA AND EDAMAME SNACK

P.T.: 10 min

C.T.: 40 min

M.C.: Roasting

SERVINGS: 4

INGR.: 1 can (15 oz.) chickpeas, rinsed and drained, 1 Cup shelled edamame, thawed if frozen, 1 Tblsp olive oil, 1 tsp ground cumin, 1/2 tsp smoked paprika, Salt and pepper to taste

DIRECTIONS:

Preheat oven to 400°F (200°C). Pat chickpeas and edamame dry with paper towels.

Toss chickpeas and edamame with olive oil, cumin, smoked paprika, salt, and pepper in a bowl.

Spread on a baking sheet in a single layer.

Roast for 30-40 minutes, stirring occasionally, until crispy and golden.

Let cool before serving.

TIPS:

Ensure chickpeas are thoroughly dried for maximum crispiness.

Store in an airtight container for up to a week for a crunchy snack.

Spice levels can be adjusted to taste, or try different seasonings for variety.

N.V.: Calories: 150, Fat: 6g, Carbs: 18g, Protein: 8g, Sugar: 3g

2. AVOCADO AND COTTAGE CHEESE STUFFED CHERRY TOMATOES

P.T.: 15 min

C.T.: 0 min

M.C.: Assembling

SERVINGS: 4

INGR.: 24 cherry tomatoes, 1 ripe avocado, mashed, 1/2 Cup cottage cheese, 1 Tblsp lemon juice, Salt and pepper to taste, Fresh herbs (such as dill or parsley) for garnish

DIRECTIONS:

Slice the tops off the cherry tomatoes and scoop out the insides with a small spoon.

In a bowl, mix mashed avocado, cottage cheese, and lemon juice. Season with salt and pepper.

Fill each cherry tomato with the avocado and cottage cheese mixture.

Garnish with fresh herbs and serve immediately.

TIPS:

Use a piping bag or a small spoon to fill the tomatoes easily.

For a dairy-free version, substitute cottage cheese with tofu or almond-based cheese.

These are best enjoyed the day they are made to ensure the tomatoes remain firm.

N.V.: Calories: 120, Fat: 8g, Carbs: 9g, Protein: 5g, Sugar: 4g

3. SWEET POTATO TOAST WITH ALMOND BUTTER AND BANANA

P.T.: 5 min

C.T.: 15 min

M.C.: Toasting

SERVINGS: 4

INGR.: 2 large sweet potatoes, sliced lengthwise into 1/4 inch thick slices, 1/4 Cup almond butter, 1 banana, sliced, Cinnamon for sprinkling, Honey for drizzling

DIRECTIONS:

Toast sweet potato slices in a toaster or toaster oven on high until tender and slightly crispy, about 2-3 cycles.

Spread almond butter on each sweet potato slice.

Top with banana slices, a sprinkle of cinnamon, and a drizzle of honey.

Serve immediately as a nutritious snack or breakfast.

TIPS:

For added texture, sprinkle with chia seeds or crushed nuts.

Sweet potato slices can also be baked in the oven at 400°F (200°C) for 15-20 minutes.

Experiment with toppings like avocado or tahini for savory options.

N.V.: Calories: 180, Fat: 8g, Carbs: 24g, Protein: 4g, Sugar: 11g

4. KALE CHIPS WITH NUTRITIONAL YEAST

P.T.: 10 min

C.T.: 20 min

M.C.: Baking

SERVINGS: 4

INGR.: 1 bunch kale, washed and dried, stems removed, leaves torn into bite-sized pieces, 2 Tblsp olive oil, 1/4 Cup nutritional yeast, Salt to taste

DIRECTIONS:

Preheat oven to 300°F (150°C). Line a baking sheet with parchment paper.

In a large bowl, toss kale pieces with olive oil until evenly coated. Sprinkle with nutritional yeast and salt, tossing again to distribute evenly.

Arrange kale in a single layer on the prepared baking sheet. Bake for 20 minutes, or until crispy, turning halfway through baking.

Let cool on the baking sheet before serving to achieve maximum crispiness.

TIPS:

Make sure the kale is thoroughly dry before adding oil to ensure it gets crispy.

Store leftover kale chips in an airtight container at room temperature for up to 2 days.

Nutritional yeast adds a cheesy flavor and

boosts the nutritional value with vitamins and minerals.

N.V.: Calories: 100, Fat: 7g, Carbs: 7g, Protein: 5g, Sugar: 0g

5. PEANUT BUTTER ENERGY BALLS

P.T.: 15 min

C.T.: 0 min

M.C.: Mixing/Refrigerating

SERVINGS: 12 balls

INGR.: 1 Cup oats, 1/2 Cup natural peanut butter, 1/3 Cup honey, 1/4 Cup flaxseed meal, 1/2 Cup mini chocolate chips, 1 tsp vanilla extract, Pinch of salt

DIRECTIONS:

In a medium bowl, mix together oats, peanut butter, honey, flaxseed meal, chocolate chips, vanilla extract, and a pinch of salt until well combined.

Roll the mixture into 1-inch balls and place on a baking sheet lined with parchment paper.

Refrigerate for at least 1 hour before serving to set.

TIPS:

For a crunchier texture, add chopped nuts like almonds or walnuts.

These energy balls can be stored in the refrigerator for up to a week or frozen for longer storage.

Substitute almond butter or cashew butter for peanut butter if desired.

N.V.: Calories: 180, Fat: 10g, Carbs: 20g, Protein: 5g, Sugar: 12g

6. BAKED APPLE CHIPS

P.T.: 15 min

C.T.: 2 hrs

M.C.: Baking

SERVINGS: 4

INGR.: 2 large apples, cored and thinly sliced, 1 tsp ground cinnamon, 1 tsp sugar (optional)

DIRECTIONS:

Preheat oven to 200°F (90°C). Line two baking sheets with parchment paper.

Arrange apple slices in a single layer on the baking sheets. Sprinkle with cinnamon and sugar if using.

Bake for 1 hour, then flip the slices and continue baking for another 1 to 1.5 hours, or until the apple slices are dried out and crisp.

Let cool completely before serving to achieve the crispiest texture.

TIPS:

Use a mandoline slicer for uniformly thin apple slices, which will bake more evenly.

Experiment with different apple varieties to find your preferred sweetness and flavor.

Apple chips can be stored in an airtight container at room temperature for up to a week.

N.V.: Calories: 50, Fat: 0g, Carbs: 13g, Protein: 0g, Sugar: 10g

1. GARLIC PARMESAN ROASTED BRUSSELS SPROUTS

P.T.: 10 min

C.T.: 20 min

M.C.: Roasting

SERVINGS: 4

INGR.: 1 lb Brussels sprouts, trimmed and halved, 2 Tblsp olive oil, 4 cloves garlic, minced, 1/4 Cup grated Parmesan cheese, Salt and pepper to taste

DIRECTIONS:

Preheat oven to 400°F (200°C). In a large bowl, toss Brussels sprouts with olive oil, garlic, salt, and pepper until well coated.

Spread the Brussels sprouts on a baking sheet in a single layer, cut side down.

Roast for 20 minutes, or until tender and caramelized on the edges.

Sprinkle with Parmesan cheese and roast for an additional 5 minutes, until cheese is melted and golden.

Serve immediately.

TIPS:

For extra crispiness, let the Brussels sprouts roast a few minutes longer before adding the cheese.

Add a squeeze of lemon juice before serving for a fresh flavor boost.

Leftovers can be reheated in an oven for best texture.

N.V.: Calories: 150, Fat: 8g, Carbs: 12g, Protein: 6g, Sugar: 3g

2. MAPLE GLAZED CARROTS

P.T.: 5 min

C.T.: 25 min

M.C.: Roasting

SERVINGS: 4

INGR.: 1 lb carrots, peeled and sliced diagonally, 2 Tblsp olive oil, 3 Tblsp maple syrup, 1 Tblsp thyme, fresh, Salt and pepper to taste

DIRECTIONS:

Preheat oven to 375°F (190°C). In a mixing bowl, toss carrots with olive oil, maple syrup, thyme, salt, and pepper.

Spread the carrots on a lined baking sheet and roast for 25 minutes, stirring halfway through, until carrots are tender and caramelized.

Adjust seasoning if necessary and serve hot.

TIPS:

Choose carrots that are similar in size for even cooking.

For a spicy twist, add a pinch of cayenne pepper to the glaze.

These carrots pair well with both poultry and pork dishes.

N.V.: Calories: 140, Fat: 7g, Carbs: 20g, Protein: 1g, Sugar: 12g

3. SPICY ROASTED CAULIFLOWER

P.T.: 10 min

C.T.: 25 min

M.C.: Roasting

SERVINGS: 4

INGR.: 1 head cauliflower, cut into florets, 2 Tblsp olive oil, 1 tsp chili powder, 1/2 tsp garlic powder, 1/4 tsp cayenne pepper, Salt to taste

DIRECTIONS:

Preheat oven to 425°F (220°C). In a large bowl, toss cauliflower florets with olive oil, chili powder, garlic powder, cayenne pepper, and salt.

Spread the florets on a baking sheet in a single layer.

Roast for 25 minutes, stirring once, until florets are golden and crispy.

Serve immediately as a spicy side dish.

TIPS:

For deeper flavor, add a squeeze of lime juice after roasting.

Experiment with other spices like curry powder or smoked paprika for variation.

Serve alongside a cooling dip like tzatziki or ranch to balance the heat.

N.V.: Calories: 120, Fat: 7g, Carbs: 13g, Protein: 4g, Sugar: 4g

WHOLE GRAIN AND LEGUME SIDES

1. QUINOA TABBOULEH

P.T.: 15 min

C.T.: 15 min

M.C.: Boiling/Chilling

SERVINGS: 4

INGR.: 1 Cup quinoa, rinsed, 2 Cups water, 1/4 Cup olive oil, 1/4 Cup lemon juice, 2 Cups parsley, finely chopped, 1 Cup tomatoes, diced, 1/2 Cup cucumber, diced, 1/4 Cup green onions, sliced, Salt and pepper to taste

DIRECTIONS:

In a medium saucepan, bring water to a boil. Add quinoa and reduce heat to low. Cover and simmer for 15 minutes or until water is absorbed. Remove from heat and let stand covered for 5 minutes. Fluff with a fork and let cool.

In a large bowl, whisk together olive oil and lemon juice. Add cooled quinoa, parsley, tomatoes, cucumber, and green onions. Toss to combine. Season with salt and pepper to taste.

Chill in the refrigerator for at least 1 hour before serving to allow flavors to meld.

TIPS:

For added crunch, include diced bell peppers.

Tabbouleh can be stored in the refrigerator for up to 3 days, making it perfect for meal prep.

Serve as a refreshing side dish or over lettuce for a light meal.

N.V.: Calories: 220, Fat: 10g, Carbs: 30g, Protein: 6g, Sugar: 2g

2. LEMON GARLIC LENTILS

P.T.: 10 min

C.T.: 25 min

M.C.: Simmering

SERVINGS: 4

INGR.: 1 Cup green lentils, rinsed, 2 Cups vegetable broth, 2 cloves garlic, minced, 1 lemon, zest and juice, 2 Tblsp olive oil, Salt and pepper to taste, 1/4 Cup parsley, chopped

DIRECTIONS:

In a saucepan, combine lentils, vegetable broth, and garlic. Bring to a boil, then reduce heat, cover, and simmer for about 25 minutes, or until lentils are tender.

Drain any excess liquid and transfer lentils to a serving bowl.

While lentils are still warm, stir in lemon zest, lemon juice, olive oil, and chopped parsley. Season with salt and pepper to taste.

Serve warm or at room temperature.

TIPS:

Add diced carrots or celery to the lentils while cooking for extra flavor and texture.

For a spicy kick, include a pinch of red pepper flakes.

This dish pairs well with grilled chicken or fish for a complete meal.

N.V.: Calories: 200, Fat: 7g, Carbs: 27g, Protein: 10g, Sugar: 2g

3. BARLEY AND MUSHROOM PILAF

P.T.: 10 min

C.T.: 40 min

M.C.: Sautéing/Boiling

SERVINGS: 4

INGR.: 1 Cup pearled barley, rinsed, 2 Tblsp olive oil, 1 onion, diced, 2 Cups mushrooms, sliced, 2 cloves garlic, minced, 3 Cups vegetable broth, Salt and pepper to taste, 1/4 Cup parsley, chopped

DIRECTIONS:

In a large skillet, heat olive oil over medium heat. Add onion and garlic, sautéing until softened.

Add mushrooms and cook until they release their moisture and begin to brown.

Stir in barley until well coated with the onion and mushroom mixture. Pour in vegetable broth and bring to a boil.

Reduce heat to low, cover, and simmer for 30-40 minutes, or until barley is tender and liquid is absorbed.

Remove from heat, stir in chopped parsley, and season with salt and pepper to taste.

TIPS:

For a nutty flavor, toast barley in the skillet for 2-3 minutes before adding broth.

Experiment with different mushroom varieties for varied flavors.

Serve as a hearty side dish with roasted meats or as a vegetarian main course.

N.V.: Calories: 240, Fat: 7g, Carbs: 40g, Protein: 6g, Sugar: 2g

4. BLACK BEAN AND CORN SALAD

P.T.: 15 min

C.T.: 0 min

M.C.: Mixing

SERVINGS: 4

INGR.: 1 can (15 oz.) black beans, rinsed and drained, 1 Cup corn kernels, fresh or frozen (thawed), 1 red bell pepper, diced, 1/4 Cup red onion, finely chopped, 1/4 Cup cilantro, chopped, 2 Tblsp lime juice, 1 Tblsp olive oil, 1/2 tsp ground cumin, Salt and pepper to taste

DIRECTIONS:

In a large bowl, combine black beans, corn, red bell pepper, red onion, and cilantro.

In a small bowl, whisk together lime juice, olive oil, ground cumin, salt, and pepper to create the dressing.

Pour the dressing over the bean mixture and toss to coat evenly.

Let the salad sit for at least 10 minutes before serving to allow flavors to meld.

TIPS:

For a spicy version, add diced jalapeño to the salad.

This salad can be served as a side dish or used as a filling for tacos or wraps.

The salad keeps well in the refrigerator, making it perfect for meal prep.

N.V.: Calories: 180, Fat: 5g, Carbs: 28g, Protein: 8g, Sugar: 4g

5. FARRO WITH ROASTED VEGETABLES

P.T.: 20 min

C.T.: 30 min

M.C.: Roasting/Boiling

SERVINGS: 4

INGR.: 1 Cup farro, rinsed, 2 Cups vegetable broth, 1 small zucchini, diced, 1 small yellow squash, diced, 1 red onion, chopped, 1 Tblsp olive oil, Salt and pepper to taste, 1/4 Cup grated Parmesan cheese, 2 Tblsp fresh basil, chopped

DIRECTIONS:

Preheat oven to 400°F (200°C). Toss zucchini, yellow squash, and red onion with olive oil, salt, and pepper. Spread on a baking sheet and roast for 20 minutes, until tender.

Meanwhile, in a saucepan, bring vegetable broth to a boil. Add farro and reduce heat to simmer. Cover and cook for 30 minutes, or until farro is tender. Drain any excess liquid.

In a large bowl, combine cooked farro with roasted vegetables. Stir in grated Parmesan cheese and fresh basil.

Serve warm as a nutritious side dish.

TIPS:

Experiment with different roasted vegetables according to season for variety.

Farro can be substituted with quinoa or barley depending on preference or availability.

For a vegan version, omit the Parmesan cheese or use a vegan alternative.

N.V.: Calories: 250, Fat: 7g, Carbs: 40g, Protein: 9g, Sugar: 5g

6. MEDITERRANEAN LENTIL SALAD

P.T.: 15 min

C.T.: 20 min

M.C.: Boiling/Mixing

SERVINGS: 4

INGR.: 1 Cup green lentils, rinsed, 1 cucumber, diced, 1 Cup cherry tomatoes, halved, 1/2 red onion, finely chopped, 1/4 Cup Kalamata olives, sliced, 1/4 Cup feta cheese, crumbled, For the dressing: 3 Tblsp olive oil, 2 Tblsp red wine vinegar, 1 tsp Dijon mustard, Salt and pepper to taste, 1 Tblsp fresh parsley, chopped

DIRECTIONS:

Cook lentils in a pot of boiling water for 20 minutes, or until tender. Drain and let cool.

In a large bowl, combine cooled lentils, cucumber, cherry tomatoes, red onion, Kalamata olives, and feta cheese.

In a small bowl, whisk together olive oil, red wine vinegar, Dijon mustard, salt, and pepper to create the dressing.

Pour the dressing over the lentil mixture and toss to combine. Sprinkle with fresh parsley before serving.

TIPS:

To add more protein, include diced grilled chicken or tofu.

This salad can be served cold, making it perfect for hot summer days or picnics.

Lentil salad can be stored in the refrigerator for up to 3 days, making it ideal for meal prep.

N.V.: Calories: 220, Fat: 10g, Carbs: 25g, Protein: 10g, Sugar: 3g

8. Desserts Without the Guilt

Fruit-Based Desserts

1. BAKED CINNAMON APPLES

P.T.: 10 min

C.T.: 30 min

M.C.: Baking

SERVINGS: 4

INGR.: 4 large apples, cored and halved, 2 Tblsp melted coconut oil, 4 tsp cinnamon, 2 Tblsp honey or maple syrup, 1/2 Cup walnuts, chopped

DIRECTIONS:

Preheat oven to 375°F (190°C). Place apple halves cut-side up on a baking tray.

Brush each apple half with melted coconut oil and sprinkle with cinnamon.

Drizzle honey or maple syrup over each apple half and top with chopped walnuts.

Bake in the preheated oven for 30 minutes or until apples are tender.

Serve warm, optionally with a dollop of Greek yogurt.

TIPS:

Choose firm apples like Granny Smith or Honeycrisp for best results.

For added flavor, mix a pinch of nutmeg or ginger into the cinnamon.

To make this vegan, ensure you use maple syrup instead of honey.

N.V.: Calories: 210, Fat: 10g, Carbs: 31g, Protein: 2g, Sugar: 23g

2. MANGO AND CHIA PUDDING

P.T.: 15 min (plus overnight chilling)

C.T.: 0 min

M.C.: Refrigerating

SERVINGS: 4

INGR.: 1 Cup coconut milk, 1/4 Cup chia seeds, 2 Tblsp honey or maple syrup, 1 tsp vanilla extract, 1 mango, peeled and diced

DIRECTIONS:

In a bowl, mix coconut milk, chia seeds, honey (or maple syrup), and vanilla extract until well combined.

Divide the mixture between four serving glasses or bowls.

Refrigerate overnight or until the chia seeds have absorbed the liquid and the pudding has thickened.

Top with diced mango before serving.

TIPS:

Stir the pudding a couple of times within the first hour of refrigerating to prevent clumping.

Substitute mango with other fruits like berries or kiwi based on season and preference.

For a creamier pudding, blend half the mango into the coconut milk before mixing with chia seeds.

N.V.: Calories: 180, Fat: 11g, Carbs: 20g, Protein: 3g, Sugar: 14g

3. PEACHES GRILLED WITH HONEY AND YOGURT

P.T.: 10 min

C.T.: 10 min

M.C.: Grilling

SERVINGS: 4

INGR.: 4 peaches, halved and pitted, 2 Tblsp honey, 1 Cup Greek yogurt, 1/4 Cup granola, 1 Tblsp fresh mint, chopped

DIRECTIONS:

Preheat grill to medium heat. Brush peach halves with honey.

Place peaches cut-side down on the grill. Grill for about 5 minutes or until grill marks appear.

Flip peaches and grill for another 5 minutes or until tender.

Serve warm peaches with a dollop of Greek yogurt, a sprinkle of granola, and chopped mint.

TIPS:

For added flavor, mix a little cinnamon or vanilla extract into the Greek yogurt.

Peaches can also be roasted in the oven at 375°F (190°C) if grilling is not an option.

Use honey or maple syrup to drizzle over the top for extra sweetness if desired.

N.V.: Calories: 150, Fat: 2g, Carbs: 29g, Protein: 6g, Sugar: 25g

LOW-SUGAR BAKED GOODS

1. ALMOND FLOUR BLUEBERRY MUFFINS

P.T.: 10 min

C.T.: 20 min

M.C.: Baking

SERVINGS: 12 muffins

INGR.: 2 Cups almond flour, 1/4 Cup coconut flour, 1 tsp baking soda, 1/4 tsp salt, 3 eggs, 1/4 Cup unsweetened almond milk, 1/4 Cup honey, 1 tsp vanilla extract, 1 Cup fresh blueberries

DIRECTIONS:

Preheat oven to 375°F (190°C). Line a muffin tin with paper liners or grease with cooking spray.

In a large bowl, whisk together almond flour, coconut flour, baking soda, and salt.

In another bowl, beat eggs, almond milk, honey, and vanilla extract until smooth.

Combine wet and dry ingredients, stirring until just mixed. Gently fold in blueberries.

Divide the batter evenly among muffin Cups, filling each about two-thirds full.

Bake for 20 minutes, or until a toothpick inserted into the center comes out clean.

Let muffins cool in the pan for 5 minutes, then transfer to a wire rack to cool completely.

TIPS:

For added lemon flavor, include 1 tsp of lemon zest to the batter.

Muffins can be stored in an airtight container at room temperature for up to 3 days or frozen for up to a month.

Ensure not to overmix the batter to keep the muffins light and fluffy.

N.V.: Calories: 160, Fat: 11g, Carbs: 12g, Protein: 6g, Sugar: 7g

2. WHOLE WHEAT BANANA BREAD

P.T.: 15 min

C.T.: 55 min

M.C.: Baking

SERVINGS: 1 loaf

INGR.: 2 Cups whole wheat flour, 1 tsp baking soda, 1/4 tsp salt, 1/2 tsp cinnamon, 3 ripe bananas, mashed, 1/3 Cup unsweetened applesauce, 1/4 Cup honey, 2 eggs, 1 tsp vanilla extract, 1/2 Cup walnuts, chopped (optional)

DIRECTIONS:

Preheat oven to 350°F (175°C). Grease a 9x5 inch loaf pan.

In a bowl, mix together whole wheat flour, baking soda, salt, and cinnamon.

In another bowl, combine mashed bananas, applesauce, honey, eggs, and vanilla extract. Add wet ingredients to dry ingredients, stirring until just combined. Fold in walnuts if using.

Pour batter into prepared loaf pan. Bake for 55 minutes, or until a toothpick inserted into the center comes out clean.

Let the bread cool in the pan for 10 minutes, then transfer to a wire rack to cool completely.

TIPS:

For a nut-free version, omit the walnuts or replace them with chocolate chips.

Banana bread can be wrapped tightly and stored at room temperature for several days or frozen for longer storage.

Adding a tablespoon of ground flaxseed can increase the fiber content.

N.V.: Calories: 190, Fat: 3g, Carbs: 36g, Protein: 5g, Sugar: 15g

3. OATMEAL PUMPKIN MUFFINS

P.T.: 15 min

C.T.: 25 min

M.C.: Baking

SERVINGS: 12 muffins

INGR.: 1 1/2 Cups rolled oats, 1 Cup whole wheat flour, 1 1/2 tsp baking powder, 1/2 tsp baking soda, 1/2 tsp salt, 1 tsp cinnamon, 1/2 tsp nutmeg, 1 Cup pumpkin puree, 3/4 Cup unsweetened almond milk, 1/2 Cup honey, 2 eggs, 1 tsp vanilla extract

DIRECTIONS:

Preheat oven to 375°F (190°C). Line a muffin tin with paper liners.

In a large bowl, combine rolled oats, whole wheat flour, baking powder, baking soda, salt, cinnamon, and nutmeg.

In another bowl, whisk together pumpkin

puree, almond milk, honey, eggs, and vanilla extract.

Mix wet ingredients into dry ingredients until just combined.

Divide the batter evenly among muffin Cups.

Bake for 25 minutes, or until a toothpick inserted into the center comes out clean.

Let muffins cool in the tin for 5 minutes, then transfer to a wire rack to cool completely.

TIPS:

Add a handful of walnuts or pecans for texture and extra flavor.

These muffins can be stored in an airtight container for up to 3 days or frozen for up to a month.

For a gluten-free version, use gluten-free oats and a gluten-free flour blend in place of whole wheat flour.

N.V.: Calories: 150, Fat: 2g, Carbs: 31g, Protein: 4g, Sugar: 16g

Sweet Snacks

1. NO-BAKE CHOCOLATE PEANUT BUTTER ENERGY BALLS

P.T.: 15 min

C.T.: 0 min

M.C.: Mixing

SERVINGS: 12 balls

INGR.: 1 Cup oats, 1/2 Cup natural peanut butter, 1/3 Cup honey, 1/4 Cup unsweetened cocoa powder, 1/2 Cup ground flaxseed, 1 tsp vanilla extract, Pinch of salt, 1/4 Cup mini chocolate chips

DIRECTIONS:

In a large bowl, mix together oats, peanut butter, honey, cocoa powder, flaxseed, vanilla extract, salt, and chocolate chips until well combined.

Chill the mixture in the refrigerator for about 10 minutes to make it easier to handle.

Roll the mixture into 12 balls and place them on a baking sheet lined with parchment paper.

Refrigerate the energy balls for at least 30 minutes before serving to set.

TIPS:

If the mixture is too sticky, add more oats or flaxseed. If too dry, add a bit more peanut butter or honey.

Store the energy balls in an airtight container in the refrigerator for up to 1 week.

For a nut-free version, substitute sunflower seed butter for peanut butter.

N.V.: Calories: 180, Fat: 10g, Carbs: 20g, Protein: 5g, Sugar: 12g

2. BAKED APPLE CHIPS WITH CINNAMON

P.T.: 10 min

C.T.: 2 hr

M.C.: Baking

SERVINGS: 4

INGR.: 2 large apples, cored and thinly sliced, 1 tsp ground cinnamon, 1/4 tsp ground nutmeg (optional)

DIRECTIONS:

Preheat your oven to 200°F (93°C). Line two baking sheets with parchment paper.

Arrange apple slices in a single layer on the baking sheets. Sprinkle evenly with cinnamon and nutmeg if using.

Bake for 1 hour, then flip the slices and continue baking for another 1 hour or until the apple chips are crisp.

Let the chips cool completely on the baking sheets before serving to crisp up further.

TIPS:

For evenly cooked chips, try to slice the apples as thinly and uniformly as possible.

Store apple chips in an airtight container at room temperature for up to 1 week.

Experiment with different spices like cardamom or clove for variety.

N.V.: Calories: 50, Fat: 0g, Carbs: 13g, Protein: 0g, Sugar: 10g

3. FROZEN YOGURT BERRIES

P.T.: 15 min

C.T.: 1 hr (freezing time)

M.C.: Freezing

SERVINGS: 4

INGR.: 1 Cup mixed berries (strawberries, blueberries, raspberries), 1 Cup Greek yogurt, 1 Tblsp honey, 1 tsp vanilla extract

DIRECTIONS:

In a bowl, mix Greek yogurt, honey, and vanilla extract until smooth.

Dip each berry into the yogurt mixture to coat completely, then place on a baking sheet lined with parchment paper.

Freeze the coated berries for at least 1 hour, or until the yogurt is firm.

Serve frozen as a refreshing and healthy snack.

TIPS:

Use a toothpick or fork to dip the berries for easier handling.

Mix in a little lemon zest to the yogurt mixture for an extra zing.

Keep the frozen yogurt berries in a sealed container in the freezer for up to 1 month.

N.V.: Calories: 70, Fat: 1g, Carbs: 12g, Protein: 4g, Sugar: 10g

4. ALMOND AND DATE TRUFFLES

P.T.: 20 min

C.T.: 0 min

M.C.: Mixing/Refrigerating

SERVINGS: 12 truffles

INGR.: 1 Cup Medjool dates, pitted, 1 Cup almonds, 1/4 Cup unsweetened cocoa powder, 1 tsp vanilla extract, A pinch of sea salt, Optional coatings: shredded coconut, cocoa powder, or crushed nuts

DIRECTIONS:

In a food processor, blend the Medjool dates and almonds until a sticky dough forms.

Add unsweetened cocoa powder, vanilla extract, and sea salt to the mixture and blend until all ingredients are well combined.

Take spoonfuls of the mixture and roll into balls. Roll each ball into your choice of optional coatings.

Place the truffles on a baking sheet lined with parchment paper and refrigerate for at least an hour before serving.

TIPS:

If the mixture is too dry, add a few drops of water to help it come together.

These truffles can be stored in an airtight container in the refrigerator for up to a week.

Experiment with different nuts like walnuts or pecans for variety.

N.V.: Calories: 150, Fat: 8g, Carbs: 18g, Protein: 4g, Sugar: 14g

5. GREEK YOGURT AND HONEY DIPPED GRAPES

P.T.: 15 min

C.T.: 2 hr (freezing time)

M.C.: Freezing

SERVINGS: 4

INGR.: 1 Cup green grapes, washed and dried, 1 Cup Greek yogurt, 2 Tblsp honey, Optional: chopped nuts or granola for coating

DIRECTIONS:

Mix Greek yogurt and honey in a bowl until well combined.

Dip each grape into the yogurt mixture, then roll in chopped nuts or granola if desired. Place on a baking sheet lined with parchment paper.

Freeze the grapes for at least 2 hours, or until the yogurt coating is firm.

Serve as a cold, refreshing snack.

TIPS:

Ensure grapes are completely dry before dipping to help the yogurt adhere better.

For a variety, mix in a little vanilla or almond extract into the yogurt.

These can be stored in the freezer in an airtight container for up to a month.

N.V.: Calories: 80, Fat: 1g, Carbs: 15g, Protein: 5g, Sugar: 12g

6. PEANUT BUTTER BANANA ROLL-UPS

P.T.: 10 min

C.T.: 0 min

M.C.: Assembling

SERVINGS: 4

INGR.: 4 whole wheat tortillas, 1/2 Cup natural peanut butter, 2 bananas, 2 Tblsp honey, Optional: a sprinkle of cinnamon or cocoa powder

DIRECTIONS:

Spread peanut butter evenly over each tortilla.

Place a whole banana near the edge of each

tortilla and drizzle with honey. Optionally, sprinkle with cinnamon or cocoa powder.

Roll up the tortillas tightly around the banana.

Slice each roll-up into 1-inch pieces and serve.

TIPS:

For a crunchier texture, add granola or chopped nuts before rolling up the tortillas.

These roll-ups can be made ahead and stored in the refrigerator for a quick snack.

Use gluten-free tortillas for a gluten-free option.

N.V.: Calories: 300, Fat: 14g, Carbs: 40g, Protein: 8g, Sugar: 20g

9. Drinks for Every Occasion

Herbal Teas and Infusions

1. SOOTHING LAVENDER TEA

P.T.: 5 min

C.T.: 10 min

M.C.: Infusing

SERVINGS: 2

INGR.: 2 Cups water, 1 Tblsp dried lavender flowers, 1 tsp honey (optional), Lemon slices for garnish

DIRECTIONS:

Bring water to a boil in a small pot.

Remove from heat and add dried lavender flowers. Cover and let steep for 5-7 minutes.

Strain the tea into Cups, discarding the lavender.

Stir in honey if desired and garnish with a slice of lemon.

TIPS:

Lavender tea is perfect for relaxation and can help promote a restful sleep.

For a stronger floral taste, allow the lavender to steep for a longer period.

Always use culinary-grade lavender to ensure it's safe for consumption.

N.V.: Calories: 0 (without honey), Fat: 0g, Carbs: 0g (1g with honey), Protein: 0g, Sugar: 1g (with honey)

2. GINGER TURMERIC TEA

P.T.: 5 min

C.T.: 15 min

M.C.: Simmering

SERVINGS: 2

INGR.: 2 Cups water, 1 inch fresh ginger root, thinly sliced, 1/2 tsp ground turmeric, 1 tsp honey (optional), Juice of 1/2 lemon

DIRECTIONS:

Combine water, ginger slices, and ground turmeric in a pot. Bring to a boil.

Reduce heat and simmer for 10 minutes.

Remove from heat, add lemon juice, and strain into Cups.

Sweeten with honey if desired.

TIPS:

This tea is known for its anti-inflammatory properties and can help boost immunity.

For added health benefits, include a pinch of black pepper to enhance turmeric absorption.

Fresh turmeric root can be used in place of ground turmeric for a more potent flavor.

N.V.: Calories: 0 (without honey), Fat: 0g, Carbs: 0g (1g with honey), Protein: 0g, Sugar: 1g (with honey)

3. PEPPERMINT LEAF TEA

P.T.: 5 min

C.T.: 10 min

M.C.: Steeping

SERVINGS: 2

INGR.: 2 Cups water, 1/4 Cup fresh peppermint leaves, Honey or lemon

(optional)

DIRECTIONS:

Boil water in a kettle or pot.

Place peppermint leaves in a teapot or directly in Cups.

Pour hot water over the leaves and let steep for 5-7 minutes.

Strain, and if desired, sweeten with honey or add a squeeze of lemon.

TIPS:

Peppermint tea is great for digestion and can offer relief from stomach discomfort.

For a colder beverage, chill the tea and serve over ice for a refreshing drink.

Experiment with blending peppermint leaves with other herbs like chamomile for a calming effect.

N.V.: Calories: 0 (without sweeteners), Fat: 0g, Carbs: 0g, Protein: 0g, Sugar: 0g

4. HIBISCUS AND ROSEHIP TEA

P.T.: 5 min

C.T.: 10 min

M.C.: Infusing

SERVINGS: 2

INGR.: 2 Tblsp dried hibiscus flowers, 2 Tblsp dried rosehip, 2 Cups boiling water

DIRECTIONS:

Mix hibiscus and rosehip in a teapot or heatproof pitcher.

Pour boiling water over the mixture.

Cover and let steep for 10 minutes.

Strain into Cups and enjoy hot or cold.

TIPS:

Add a cinnamon stick during steeping for a spiced flavor.

Sweeten with honey or enjoy the natural tartness.

N.V.: Calories: 0, Fat: 0g, Carbs: 0g, Protein: 0g, Sugar: 0g

5. TURMERIC AND CINNAMON INFUSION

P.T.: 5 min

C.T.: 10 min

M.C.: Infusing

SERVINGS: 2

INGR.: 1 tsp ground turmeric, 1/2 tsp ground cinnamon, 1/4 tsp black pepper, 2 Cups boiling water, honey to taste

DIRECTIONS:

Combine turmeric, cinnamon, and black pepper in a teapot or heatproof pitcher.

Pour boiling water over the spices.

Cover and let steep for 10 minutes.

Strain into Cups, add honey to taste, and serve.

TIPS:

Black pepper enhances the absorption of

curcumin from turmeric.

Milk or a milk alternative can be added to create a creamy latte.

N.V.: Calories: 20, Fat: 0g, Carbs: 5g, Protein: 0g, Sugar: 5g

6. GREEN TEA WITH MINT AND LIME

P.T.: 5 min

C.T.: 3 min

M.C.: Infusing

SERVINGS: 2

INGR.: 2 green tea bags, 10 fresh mint leaves, juice of 1 lime, 2 Cups boiling water, honey to taste

DIRECTIONS:

Place tea bags and mint leaves in a teapot or heatproof pitcher.

Pour boiling water over the tea bags and mint.

Let steep for 3 minutes, then remove the tea bags.

Add lime juice and sweeten with honey as desired.

Serve hot or chilled.

TIPS:

For a cold version, refrigerate for at least 1 hour and serve over ice.

Adjust the strength of the green tea by steeping for more or less time.

N.V.: Calories: 15, Fat: 0g, Carbs: 4g, Protein: 0g, Sugar: 4g

LOW-SUGAR BEVERAGES

1. BERRY ANTIOXIDANT SMOOTHIE

P.T.: 5 min

C.T.: 0 min

M.C.: Blending

SERVINGS: 2

INGR.: 1 Cup frozen mixed berries (strawberries, blueberries, raspberries, and blackberries), 1 banana, peeled, 1/2 Cup unsweetened almond milk, 1/2 Cup Greek yogurt, 1 tablespoon chia seeds, 1 tablespoon honey (optional)

DIRECTIONS:

Combine all ingredients in a blender.

Blend on high speed until smooth.

Serve immediately, garnished with a few whole berries on top if desired.

TIPS:

For a vegan version, use plant-based yogurt and substitute honey with maple syrup.

Add a handful of spinach for an extra nutrient boost without altering the taste much.

N.V.: Calories: 220, Fat: 3g, Carbs: 42g, Protein: 10g, Sugar: 28g

2. GREEN DETOX SMOOTHIE

P.T.: 5 min

C.T.: 0 min

M.C.: Blending

SERVINGS: 2

INGR.:

2 Cups fresh spinach, 1 Cup cucumber, chopped, 1 apple, cored and chopped, 1/2 avocado, 1 tablespoon fresh ginger, grated, 2 tablespoons lemon juice, 1 Cup cold water

DIRECTIONS:

Place all ingredients in a blender.

Blend until smooth and creamy.

Serve chilled, with a slice of lemon for garnish.

TIPS:

If the smoothie is too thick, add more water to reach desired consistency.

For added sweetness, include a small pear or a few pineapple chunks.

N.V.: Calories: 180, Fat: 7g, Carbs: 27g, Protein: 3g, Sugar: 15g

3. PROTEIN-PACKED PEANUT BUTTER SMOOTHIE

P.T.: 5 min

C.T.: 0 min

M.C.: Blending

SERVINGS: 2

INGR.: 2 bananas, peeled and frozen, 2 tablespoons natural peanut butter, 1 Cup unsweetened almond milk, 1/2 Cup Greek yogurt, 2 tablespoons flaxseed meal, 1 scoop vanilla protein powder

DIRECTIONS:

Add all ingredients to a blender.

Blend on high until creamy and smooth.

Serve immediately, optionally topped with a sprinkle of granola.

TIPS:

Freeze the bananas ahead of time for a thicker smoothie.

Substitute almond milk with any other plant-based milk if desired.

N.V.: Calories: 350, Fat: 14g, Carbs: 40g, Protein: 25g, Sugar: 22g

NUTRITIOUS SMOOTHIES

1. TROPICAL MORNING SMOOTHIE

P.T.: 5 min

C.T.: 0 min

M.C.: Blending

SERVINGS: 2

INGR.: 1 Cup fresh pineapple, chopped, 1 mango, peeled and chopped, 1 banana, sliced, 1/2 Cup coconut milk, juice of 1 lime, 1/2 Cup ice cubes (Optional: 1 tsp chia seeds for added fiber)

DIRECTIONS:

Combine pineapple, mango, banana, coconut milk, lime juice, and ice cubes in a blender.

Blend on high until smooth. If using, add chia seeds and pulse a few times to mix.

Serve immediately, garnished with a slice of lime or pineapple if desired.

TIPS:

For an extra protein boost, add a scoop of your favorite plant-based protein powder.

If the smoothie is too thick, add a little water

or more coconut milk to achieve your desired consistency.

N.V.: Calories: 250, Fat: 7g, Carbs: 45g, Protein: 3g, Sugar: 30g

2. ANTIOXIDANT BERRY WALNUT SMOOTHIE

P.T.: 5 min

C.T.: 0 min

M.C.: Blending

SERVINGS: 2

INGR.: 1 Cup frozen mixed berries (blueberries, raspberries, blackberries), 1/2 Cup Greek yogurt, 1/4 Cup walnuts, 1 Tblsp honey, 1/2 Cup almond milk

Optional: 1 Tblsp ground flaxseed

DIRECTIONS:

Add all ingredients to a blender, starting with the almond milk to facilitate blending.

Blend until smooth, adding more almond milk if necessary to reach desired consistency.

Serve immediately, optionally sprinkled with a few whole berries or additional walnuts.

TIPS:

Soaking the walnuts for a few hours or overnight can make the smoothie creamier and increase nutrient absorption.

Adjust the sweetness by adding more or less honey, according to taste.

N.V.: Calories: 290, Fat: 15g, Carbs: 34g, Protein: 9g, Sugar: 22g

3. SPINACH AVOCADO GREEN SMOOTHIE

P.T.: 5 min

C.T.: 0 min

M.C.: Blending

SERVINGS: 2

INGR.: 2 Cups fresh spinach, 1 ripe avocado, pitted and scooped, 1/2 green apple, cored and chopped, 1/2 cucumber, chopped, Juice of 1 lemon, 1 Cup water or coconut water, Ice cubes (optional)

DIRECTIONS:

Place spinach, avocado, apple, cucumber, and lemon juice in a blender. Add water or coconut water.

Blend on high until smooth. Add ice cubes if a colder smoothie is desired and blend again. Taste and adjust the lemon juice or sweetness as needed. Serve immediately.

TIPS:

For added sweetness, include a small pear or a few stevia drops.

This smoothie is highly customizable; try adding ginger or celery for extra flavor and benefits.

N.V.: Calories: 210, Fat: 14g, Carbs: 22g, Protein: 3g, Sugar: 9g

4. SUNRISE CITRUS AND CARROT SMOOTHIE

P.T.: 5 min

C.T.: 0 min

M.C.: Blending

SERVINGS: 2

INGR.:

2 large carrots, peeled and chopped

1 orange, peeled and sectioned, 1/2 mango, peeled and cubed, Juice of 1/2 lemon, 1 inch piece of ginger, peeled, 1 Cup water or orange juice, Ice cubes, optional

DIRECTIONS:

Combine carrots, orange, mango, lemon juice, ginger, and water (or orange juice) in a blender.

Blend on high until completely smooth. Add ice cubes if you prefer a colder drink.

Serve immediately, garnished with an orange slice or a sprig of fresh mint for an extra touch of freshness.

TIPS:

Add a tablespoon of flaxseed or chia seeds for an extra fiber boost.

If the smoothie is too thick, add more water or orange juice to achieve your desired consistency.

N.V.: Calories: 180, Fat: 0.5g, Carbs: 44g, Protein: 3g, Sugar: 32g

5. CREAMY BLUEBERRY OATMEAL SMOOTHIE

P.T.: 5 min

C.T.: 0 min

M.C.: Blending

SERVINGS: 2

INGR.: 1 Cup frozen blueberries, 1/2 Cup rolled oats, 1 banana, 1 Cup almond milk, 1/2 Cup Greek yogurt, 1 Tblsp honey or maple syrup, 1/2 tsp vanilla extract

DIRECTIONS:

Soak the rolled oats in almond milk for about 5 minutes to soften.

Add soaked oats and almond milk to the blender with the remaining ingredients.

Blend until smooth and creamy.

Taste and adjust sweetness if necessary. Serve chilled.

TIPS:

For a gluten-free option, ensure the rolled oats are certified gluten-free.

Substitute blueberries with any other frozen berry for variety.

N.V.: Calories: 250, Fat: 3g, Carbs: 49g, Protein: 10g, Sugar: 23g

6. PEACH GINGER DETOX SMOOTHIE

P.T.: 5 min

C.T.: 0 min

M.C.: Blending

SERVINGS: 2

INGR.: 2 ripe peaches, sliced and pit removed, 1 inch ginger, peeled, 1 Cup spinach leaves, 1/2 cucumber, sliced, 1 Cup coconut water, Juice of 1 lime, Ice cubes, optional

DIRECTIONS:

Place all ingredients into a blender, adding the ice cubes last if using.

Blend on high speed until smooth and vibrant in color.

Serve immediately, enjoying the refreshing and cleansing benefits.

TIPS:

Freeze the peaches ahead of time for an icier texture.

A pinch of turmeric can be added for its anti-inflammatory properties.

N.V.: Calories: 120, Fat: 0.5g, Carbs: 28g, Protein: 2g, Sugar: 20g

10. Special Occasions

Festive Meals and How to Approach Them

1. ROASTED BUTTERNUT SQUASH WITH CRANBERRY QUINOA STUFFING

P.T.: 20 min

C.T.: 40 min

M.C.: Roasting/Baking

SERVINGS: 6

INGR.: 3 Cups butternut squash, cubed, 1 tblsp olive oil, salt and pepper to taste, 1 Cup quinoa, 2 Cups vegetable broth, 1/2 Cup dried cranberries, 1/2 Cup pecans, chopped, 1/4 Cup fresh parsley, chopped, 1 tsp orange zest, juice of half an orange

DIRECTIONS:

Preheat oven to 400°F (200°C). Toss butternut squash cubes with olive oil, salt, and pepper. Spread on a baking sheet and roast for 25 minutes, or until tender and caramelized.

While the squash is roasting, rinse quinoa under cold water. In a saucepan, bring vegetable broth to a boil. Add quinoa, reduce heat, cover, and simmer for 15 minutes, or until liquid is absorbed.

Fluff quinoa with a fork and mix in roasted butternut squash, dried cranberries, pecans, parsley, orange zest, and orange juice.

Adjust seasoning with salt and pepper, and serve warm as a festive side dish.

TIPS:

For added flavor, sauté a chopped onion and garlic in olive oil before adding the quinoa and broth.

This dish can easily become a main course by adding chickpeas or diced cooked chicken.

N.V.: Calories: 280, Fat: 8g, Carbs: 48g, Protein: 6g, Sugar: 12g

2. HONEY GLAZED HAM WITH CLOVES AND ORANGE JUICE

P.T.: 15 min

C.T.: 2 hr

M.C.: Baking

SERVINGS: 8

INGR.: 1 (5 to 6 lb) bone-in ham, 1 Cup honey, 1/2 Cup brown sugar, 1/2 Cup orange juice, 2 Tblsp Dijon mustard, whole cloves for studding

DIRECTIONS:

Preheat oven to 325°F (165°C). Score the surface of the ham in a diamond pattern and stud with cloves.

In a small saucepan, combine honey, brown sugar, orange juice, and Dijon mustard. Warm over low heat until well mixed.

Place ham in a roasting pan and brush with half of the glaze. Cover with foil and bake for 1.5 hours.

Remove foil, brush with remaining glaze, and increase oven temperature to 400°F (200°C). Bake for an additional 30 minutes, or until ham is golden and crispy.

Let rest for 10 minutes before slicing and serving.

TIPS:

Baste the ham every 20 minutes with the pan juices for extra flavor.

Serve with roasted vegetables or a green salad for a complete festive meal.

N.V.: Calories: 630, Fat: 20g, Carbs: 48g, Protein: 70g, Sugar: 42g

3. MEDITERRANEAN STUFFED BELL PEPPERS

P.T.: 15 min

C.T.: 30 min

M.C.: Baking

SERVINGS: 4

INGR.: 4 large bell peppers, any color, tops removed and seeded, 1 Cup cooked quinoa, 1 can (15 oz) chickpeas, rinsed and drained, 1 Cup cherry tomatoes, halved, 1/2 Cup feta cheese, crumbled, 1/4 Cup olives, sliced, 1/4 Cup red onion, finely chopped, 2 tblsp olive oil, 1 tblsp lemon juice, 1 tsp dried oregano, salt and pepper to taste

DIRECTIONS:

Preheat oven to 375°F (190°C). Place the bell peppers in a baking dish.

In a bowl, mix the quinoa, chickpeas, cherry tomatoes, feta cheese, olives, and red onion.

Whisk together olive oil, lemon juice, oregano, salt, and pepper in a small bowl. Pour over the quinoa mixture and stir to combine.

Stuff each bell pepper with the quinoa mixture. Bake for 30 minutes, or until the peppers are tender and the filling is heated through.

TIPS:

For a vegan option, replace feta cheese with a dairy-free cheese or nutritional yeast.

Add chopped spinach or kale to the stuffing for extra greens.

N.V.: Calories: 320, Fat: 14g, Carbs: 42g, Protein: 12g, Sugar: 8g

4. GARLIC AND HERB ROASTED TURKEY BREAST

P.T.: 20 min

C.T.: 1 hr 30 min

M.C.: Roasting

SERVINGS: 6

INGR.: 1 turkey breast (about 3 lbs), bone-in, skin-on, 4 tblsp unsalted butter, softened, 2 cloves garlic, minced, 1 tblsp fresh rosemary, chopped, 1 tblsp fresh thyme, chopped, 1 tblsp fresh sage, chopped, salt and pepper to taste

DIRECTIONS:

Preheat oven to 350°F (175°C). In a small bowl, mix butter with garlic, rosemary, thyme, sage, salt, and pepper.

Loosen the skin from the turkey breast and spread half of the butter mixture under the skin. Spread the rest over the outside of the turkey breast.

Roast in the preheated oven for about 1 hour and 30 minutes, or until the internal temperature reaches 165°F (74°C).

Let the turkey rest for 10 minutes before slicing.

TIPS:

Baste the turkey breast with pan juices every 30 minutes for additional flavor and moisture.

Serve with a side of cranberry sauce and roasted vegetables for a complete festive meal.

N.V.: Calories: 330, Fat: 14g, Carbs: 0g, Protein: 50g, Sugar: 0g

5. WILD RICE AND CRANBERRY PILAF

P.T.: 10 min

C.T.: 45 min

M.C.: Boiling/Sautéing

SERVINGS: 6

INGR.: 1 Cup wild rice, rinsed, 3 Cups vegetable broth, 1/2 Cup dried cranberries, 1/2 Cup pecans, toasted and chopped, 1 tblsp olive oil, 1 small onion, diced, 2 cloves garlic, minced, salt and pepper to taste

DIRECTIONS:

In a saucepan, bring vegetable broth to a boil. Add wild rice, reduce heat to low, cover, and simmer for 45 minutes, or until the rice is tender and the liquid is absorbed.

While the rice cooks, heat olive oil in a skillet over medium heat. Sauté onion and garlic until soft and translucent.

Once the rice is cooked, fluff it with a fork and transfer it to a large bowl. Add the sautéed onion and garlic, dried cranberries, and toasted pecans. Mix well.

Season with salt and pepper to taste. Serve warm.

TIPS:

For added flavor, stir in a tablespoon of orange zest or a splash of orange juice before serving.

This pilaf pairs wonderfully with roasted meats or can be enjoyed as a vegetarian main course.

N.V.: Calories: 210, Fat: 9g, Carbs: 30g, Protein: 6g, Sugar: 10g

HEALTHY HOLIDAY TREATS

1. GINGERBREAD OATMEAL COOKIES

P.T.: 15 min

C.T.: 10 min

M.C.: Baking

SERVINGS: 12 cookies

INGR.: 1 Cup rolled oats, 3/4 Cup whole wheat flour, 1/4 Cup almond flour, 1 tsp baking powder, 2 tsp ground ginger, 1 tsp cinnamon, 1/4 tsp nutmeg, 1/4 Cup unsweetened applesauce, 1/4 Cup molasses, 1 egg, 1 tsp vanilla extract

DIRECTIONS:

Preheat oven to 350°F (175°C). Line a baking sheet with parchment paper.

In a large bowl, mix together the oats, whole

wheat flour, almond flour, baking powder, ginger, cinnamon, and nutmeg.

In another bowl, whisk together the applesauce, molasses, egg, and vanilla extract until well combined.

Add the wet ingredients to the dry ingredients and stir until just combined.

Drop tablespoon-sized amounts of dough onto the prepared baking sheet. Flatten slightly with the back of the spoon.

Bake for 10-12 minutes or until the edges start to turn golden brown. Let cool on the baking sheet for 5 minutes before transferring to a wire rack to cool completely.

TIPS:

For a vegan version, substitute the egg with a flax egg (1 Tblsp ground flaxseed mixed with 3 Tblsp water, let sit for 15 minutes).

Add a handful of raisins or dried cranberries for extra sweetness if desired.

N.V.: Calories: 110, Fat: 2g, Carbs: 20g, Protein: 3g, Sugar: 7g

2. CHOCOLATE PEPPERMINT ENERGY BALLS

P.T.: 20 min

C.T.: 0 min

M.C.: Mixing/Refrigerating

SERVINGS: 15 balls

INGR.: 1 Cup dates, pitted, 1/2 Cup almonds, 1/4 Cup cocoa powder, 1/4 tsp peppermint extract, pinch of salt, crushed candy canes for coating (optional)

DIRECTIONS:

In a food processor, blend dates and almonds until a sticky dough forms.

Add cocoa powder, peppermint extract, and a pinch of salt. Process again until all ingredients are well combined.

Roll the mixture into small balls, about 1 inch in diameter.

If using, roll the balls in crushed candy canes for a festive touch.

Refrigerate for at least an hour before serving.

TIPS:

For a smoother texture, soak the dates in warm water for 10 minutes before processing.

Store in an airtight container in the refrigerator for up to a week.

N.V.: Calories: 70, Fat: 3g, Carbs: 10g, Protein: 2g, Sugar: 7g

3. PUMPKIN SPICE MINI MUFFINS

P.T.: 10 min

C.T.: 15 min

M.C.: Baking

SERVINGS: 24 mini muffins

INGR.: 1 Cup pumpkin puree, 1/4 Cup coconut oil, melted, 1/4 Cup maple syrup, 1 egg, 1 Cup whole wheat flour, 1/2 tsp baking soda, 1 tsp pumpkin pie spice, 1/4 tsp salt

DIRECTIONS:

Preheat oven to 350°F (175°C). Grease or line a mini muffin tin.

In a bowl, mix together pumpkin puree, coconut oil, maple syrup, and egg.

In another bowl, whisk together flour, baking soda, pumpkin pie spice, and salt.

Combine the wet and dry ingredients and stir until just mixed.

Spoon the batter into the muffin tin, filling each Cup about three-quarters full.

Bake for 15 minutes or until a toothpick inserted into the center comes out clean.

Let cool in the pan for 5 minutes before transferring to a wire rack to cool completely.

TIPS:

Add a handful of chopped nuts or chocolate chips to the batter for extra texture and flavor.

Substitute the egg with a flax egg for a vegan version.

N.V.: Calories: 60, Fat: 3g, Carbs: 8g, Protein: 1g, Sugar: 4g

Entertaining with Diabetes-Friendly Dishes

1. ZUCCHINI NOODLES WITH AVOCADO PESTO

P.T.: 15 min

C.T.: 0 min

M.C.: Spiralizing/Blending

SERVINGS: 4

INGR.: 4 large zucchinis, 1 ripe avocado, 1/2 Cup fresh basil leaves, 2 cloves garlic, 1/4 Cup pine nuts, 2 tblsp lemon juice
salt and pepper to taste, cherry tomatoes for garnish

DIRECTIONS:

Use a spiralizer to turn the zucchinis into noodles. Place them in a large bowl.

In a food processor, combine avocado, basil, garlic, pine nuts, lemon juice, salt, and pepper. Blend until smooth.

Toss the zucchini noodles with the avocado pesto until well coated.

Serve garnished with cherry tomatoes and additional pine nuts if desired.

TIPS:

For a protein boost, add grilled chicken or shrimp on top.

Keep the zucchini noodles raw for a crunchy texture, or sauté them briefly for a softer noodle.

N.V.: Calories: 220, Fat: 16g, Carbs: 16g, Protein: 6g, Sugar: 5g

2. QUINOA SALAD WITH BLACK BEANS AND MANGO

P.T.: 20 min

C.T.: 15 min

M.C.: Boiling/Mixing

SERVINGS: 6

INGR.:

1 Cup quinoa, 2 Cups water, 1 can (15 oz)

black beans, rinsed and drained, 1 large mango, diced, 1 red bell pepper, diced, 1/4 Cup fresh cilantro, chopped, 1 lime, juiced, salt and pepper to taste

DIRECTIONS:

Rinse quinoa under cold water. In a medium pot, bring 2 Cups of water to a boil. Add quinoa, reduce heat, cover, and simmer for 15 minutes. Let it cool.

In a large bowl, combine cooled quinoa, black beans, mango, red bell pepper, and cilantro.

Add lime juice, salt, and pepper. Toss everything together until well mixed.

Chill before serving to allow flavors to meld.

TIPS:

For added crunch, include diced cucumber or sliced almonds.

Can be served as a main dish or a side salad.

N.V.: Calories: 200, Fat: 2g, Carbs: 40g, Protein: 8g, Sugar: 9g

3. BAKED SALMON WITH DIJON CRUST

P.T.: 10 min

C.T.: 20 min

M.C.: Baking

SERVINGS: 4

INGR.: 4 salmon fillets (6 oz each), 2 tblsp dijon mustard, 1/4 Cup almond flour, 1 tblsp olive oil, 1 tblsp fresh dill, chopped, salt and pepper to taste

DIRECTIONS:

Preheat oven to 400°F (200°C). Line a baking sheet with parchment paper.

Place salmon fillets on the prepared baking sheet. Season with salt and pepper. Spread Dijon mustard on top of each fillet.

In a small bowl, mix almond flour, olive oil, and dill. Sprinkle this mixture over the mustard-covered salmon.

Bake for 20 minutes or until the salmon flakes easily with a fork.

TIPS:

For extra flavor, add minced garlic or lemon zest to the crust mixture.

Serve with a side of steamed vegetables or a fresh green salad.

N.V.: Calories: 290, Fat: 18g, Carbs: 3g, Protein: 28g, Sugar: 0g

PART III: 45-DAY MEAL PLAN

11. 45-Day Meal Plan

Weekly Shopping Lists

Fruits and Vegetables

- Avocados
- Bananas
- Berries (blueberries, strawberries, raspberries, blackberries)
- Sweet potatoes
- Spinach
- Kale
- Mixed salad greens
- Carrots
- Lemons
- Apples
- Oranges
- Peaches
- Cherry tomatoes
- Cucumbers
- Bell peppers (various colors)
- Red onions
- Garlic
- Ginger
- Fresh herbs (parsley, rosemary, thyme, sage, cilantro)
- Zucchini
- Butternut squash
- Cauliflower
- Mushrooms
- Broccoli

Proteins

- Eggs
- Chicken breasts
- Salmon fillets
- Turkey bacon
- Chicken sausage

- Cottage cheese
- Greek yogurt
- Turkey (deli slices)
- Tilapia fillets

Grains and Nuts

- Rolled oats
- Quinoa
- Whole wheat flour
- Almond flour
- Whole grain bread
- Wild rice
- Pecans
- Almonds
- Walnuts

Dairy and Eggs

- Feta cheese
- Parmesan cheese
- Mozzarella cheese
- Unsalted butter
- Milk (or almond milk, coconut milk for non-dairy options)

Canned and Jarred Goods

- Chickpeas
- Black beans
- White beans
- Lentils
- Diced tomatoes
- Coconut milk
- Vegetable broth
- Capers

Condiments and Spices

- Olive oil
- Coconut oil
- Balsamic vinegar
- Honey

- Maple syrup
- Vanilla extract
- Cocoa powder
- Dijon mustard
- Soy sauce or tamari
- Pumpkin pie spice
- Cinnamon
- Nutmeg
- Salt and pepper

Miscellaneous

- Dark chocolate chips
- Dried cranberries
- Flaxseeds or chia seeds
- Tahini

DAILY MEAL PLANNING GUIDE

Week 1-2

Day	Breakfast	Lunch	Dinner
Monday	Morning glow smoothie	Summer berry spinach salad	Roasted cauliflower steaks with tahini sauce
Tuesday	Blueberry omega boost	Crisp cucumber and radish salad	Zucchini noodles with avocado pesto
Wednesday	Green detox juice	Avocado and black bean salad	Sweet potato and black bean bowl
Thursday	Protein-packed chocolate almond smoothie	Tuscan white bean soup	Herb-crusted salmon
Friday	Coconut chia oatmeal	Classic chicken noodle soup	Lemon garlic chicken breasts
Saturday	Almond berry porridge	Roasted butternut squash soup	Spiced turkey meatballs
Sunday	Savory miso oatmeal	Spicy lentil and tomato soup	Cauliflower rice stir-fry

Week 3-4

Day	Breakfast	Lunch	Dinner
Monday	Pumpkin spice porridge	Summer berry spinach salad	Roasted cauliflower steaks with tahini sauce
Tuesday	Chocolate peanut butter banana oatmeal	Crisp cucumber and radish salad	Zucchini noodles with avocado pesto
Wednesday	Spinach and feta omelette	Avocado and black bean salad	Sweet potato and black bean bowl
Thursday	Turkey bacon and egg muffins	Tuscan white bean soup	Herb-crusted salmon
Friday	Avocado and egg breakfast wrap	Classic chicken noodle soup	Lemon garlic chicken breasts
Saturday	Smoked salmon and cream cheese scramble	Roasted butternut squash soup	Spiced turkey meatballs
Sunday	Chicken sausage and vegetable skillet	Spicy lentil and tomato soup	Cauliflower rice stir-fry

Week 5-6

Day	Breakfast	Lunch	Dinner
Monday	Berry almond overnight oats	Mixed bean salad	Grilled salmon with mango salsa
Tuesday	Quinoa fruit salad	Grilled chicken caesar salad	Vegan chili
Wednesday	Veggie-packed feta frittata	Vegetable lentil soup	Lemon-herb chicken breasts
Thursday	Cinnamon apple porridge	Turkey and avocado wrap	Stuffed bell peppers
Friday	Avocado toast with poached egg	Caprese salad with balsamic glaze	Thai curry vegetable soup
Saturday	Cottage cheese and peach parfait	Roasted vegetable quinoa bowl	Baked tilapia with lemon and capers
Sunday	Sweet potato hash with egg	Asian chicken salad	Ratatouille

Tips for Meal Prepping

Start with a Plan

Before you even preheat your oven or chop your first vegetable, take a moment to plan. Look at your week ahead and decide how many meals you'll need to prepare. Consider your schedule: Will you be home for dinner each night, or do you need to pack meals to go? Once you have a clear picture, select recipes that fit your dietary needs and personal taste. It's helpful to choose recipes with overlapping ingredients to minimize waste and streamline your cooking process.

Embrace Versatility

When selecting recipes, lean towards dishes that can be easily repurposed. For instance, a batch of quinoa cooked on Sunday can be a side for grilled chicken on Monday, mixed into a salad on Tuesday, and become part of a stuffed pepper filling on Wednesday. By preparing versatile base ingredients, you have the foundation for several meals, reducing the time you spend cooking throughout the week.

Invest in Quality Containers

Good storage containers are essential for meal prepping success. They keep your food fresh, prevent leaks, and are crucial for portion control. Opt for glass or BPA-free plastic containers that can go from freezer to microwave or oven. Having a variety of sizes for different types of meals, such as larger ones for salads and smaller ones for snacks or dressings, will make packing and eating your meals easier.

Batch Cook and Assemble

Set aside a block of time to cook your meals in batches. This is where your oven and slow cooker can become your best friends. Roasting multiple trays of vegetables, baking several chicken breasts, or simmering a large pot of stew allows you to prepare multiple servings at once. Once your components are cooked, assemble your meals into containers. If you enjoy variety, mix and match your proteins, vegetables, and grains to create different combinations for each day.

Don't Forget About Snacks

Healthy snacking is an integral part of managing diabetes, as it can help maintain blood sugar levels throughout the day. Prepare snack-sized portions of nuts, cut vegetables, cheese, or whole fruits, and pack them in grab-and-go containers. Having these ready-to-eat options available prevents the temptation to reach for less healthy snacks.

Make Friends with Your Freezer

Not all meals have to be eaten the same week they're prepared. Freezing portions for future weeks is a great way to diversify your meals and always have a backup plan. Soups, stews, casseroles, and even cooked grains freeze well. Just be sure to label your containers with the date and contents to keep track of what you have on hand.

Keep It Simple

Meal prepping doesn't have to be complicated. Simple dishes often mean fewer ingredients and less time cooking. Start with recipes you're comfortable with and that you know you enjoy. As you become more accustomed to meal prepping, you can start to experiment with new recipes and ingredients.

Listen to Your Body

As you meal prep, remember that managing diabetes is about more than just avoiding sugar. Pay attention to how different foods affect your body and blood sugar levels. Adjust your meal plans based on what you learn about your reactions to various foods. This personalized approach is key to finding a sustainable and enjoyable eating pattern.

Stay Hydrated

While focusing on food, don't forget about your fluid intake. Drinking enough water is crucial for overall health and can help manage blood sugar levels. Include a bottle of water with each meal prep, or have a reusable water bottle that you carry with you throughout the day.

Enjoy the Process

Finally, make meal prepping enjoyable. Listen to music, podcasts, or an audiobook while you cook. Involve family members in the planning and prepping process. View this time as an investment in your health and wellbeing, not just a weekly chore. Celebrate the flavors and the nourishing qualities of the food you're preparing. This positive mindset will make meal prepping something you look forward to each week.

MEASUREMENT CONVERSION TABLE

Volume Conversions

American Units	Metric Units
1 teaspoon (tsp)	5 milliliters (mL)
1 tablespoon (Tblsp)	15 milliliters (mL)
1 fluid ounce (fl oz)	30 milliliters (mL)
1 Cup	240 milliliters (mL)
1 pint (pt)	473 milliliters (mL)
1 quart (qt)	946 milliliters (mL)
1 gallon (gal)	3.785 liters (L)

Weight Conversions

American Units	Metric Units
1 ounce (oz)	28 grams (g)
1 pound (lb)	454 grams (g)

Length Conversions

American Units	Metric Units
1 inch (in)	2.54 centimeters (cm)

Temperature Conversions

To convert temperatures from Fahrenheit (°F) to Celsius (°C), you can use the following formula:

°C = (°F - 32) x 5/9

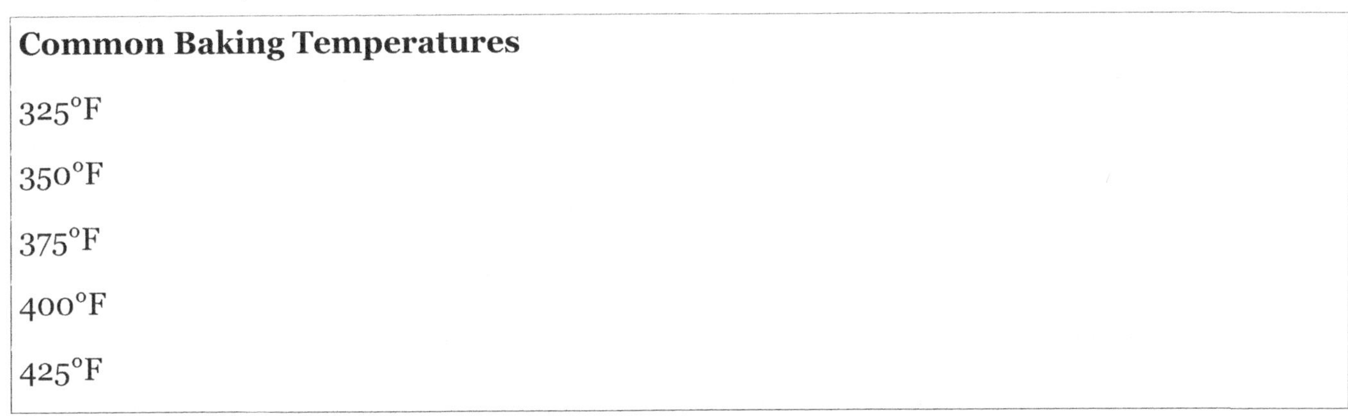

Common Baking Temperatures
325°F
350°F
375°F
400°F
425°F

Common Ingredient Conversions

Here are conversions for some common ingredients used in baking and cooking:

Ingredient	Cups to Grams
All-purpose flour	1 Cup = 120 g
Sugar (granulated)	1 Cup = 200 g
Butter	1 Cup = 227 g
Cocoa powder	1 Cup = 100 g

PART IV: BEYOND THE KITCHEN

12. Living with Type 2 Diabetes

Lifestyle Tips for Managing Diabetes

Regular Physical Activity

Incorporate regular exercise into your routine, aiming for at least 30 minutes of moderate activity most days of the week. Whether it's walking, swimming, cycling, or a yoga class, find activities you enjoy. Physical activity helps control blood sugar levels, boosts your heart health, and can contribute to weight loss, significantly impacting diabetes management.

Monitor Your Blood Sugar

Keeping a close eye on your blood sugar levels is crucial. It helps you understand how different foods, activities, and stress levels affect your body. Use a blood glucose monitor as recommended by your healthcare provider and maintain a log. This record is invaluable for identifying patterns and making necessary adjustments to your lifestyle or medication.

Stay Hydrated

Proper hydration is key to helping your body regulate blood sugar levels. Water is the best choice, as it doesn't add extra sugar to your diet. Aim to drink at least 8 glasses of water a day, and remember that needs can vary based on activity level and climate.

Get Quality Sleep

Never underestimate the power of a good night's sleep. Lack of sleep can affect your body's ability to use insulin effectively and could lead to unhealthy eating habits, impacting blood sugar control. Establish a relaxing nighttime routine and aim for 7-9 hours of sleep per night.

Manage Stress

Stress has a direct impact on blood sugar levels. Find stress-reduction techniques that work for you, such as deep breathing, meditation, journaling, or spending time in nature. Regular exercise also doubles as a great stress reliever.

Avoid Smoking and Limit Alcohol

Smoking increases the risk of diabetes complications, including heart disease, kidney disease, and nerve damage. If you smoke, seek resources to help you quit. When it comes to alcohol, moderation is key. Alcohol can affect blood sugar levels, so if you choose to drink, do so responsibly and always with food to prevent hypoglycemia.

Regular Check-ups

Stay on top of your health by scheduling regular check-ups with your healthcare team. This includes not just your primary care physician but also specialists like an endocrinologist, dietitian, and perhaps a podiatrist or ophthalmologist. These visits are crucial for monitoring your condition and preventing complications.

Stay Informed and Connected

Educate yourself about Type 2 diabetes. Understanding your condition empowers you to make informed decisions about your health. Additionally, consider joining a support group or online community. Connecting with others who are navigating similar challenges can provide invaluable support, motivation, and tips.

Foot Care

Diabetes can lead to nerve damage and reduced blood flow to your feet, making them more vulnerable to infections and other problems. Check your feet daily for cuts, blisters, red spots, and swelling. Wear comfortable shoes that fit well, and never walk barefoot. Consult your doctor at the first sign of any foot issues.

Mindful Eating

Adopt a mindful approach to eating. Listen to your body's hunger and fullness cues, eat slowly, and enjoy your food without distractions like TV or smartphones. This can help prevent overeating and improve your relationship with food, making it easier to stick to your diabetes-friendly diet.

Embrace a Positive Outlook

Finally, approach your diabetes management with a positive and proactive mindset. Celebrate small victories, stay focused on your goals, and be kind to yourself on tougher days. Remember, managing diabetes is a journey, not a destination, and every step forward is progress.

Exercise Recommendations

Finding Your Fit

The first step in incorporating exercise into your life is to find activities you genuinely enjoy. The joy of movement comes in many forms—walking in nature, dancing in your living room, cycling through the park, or practicing yoga. The key is to start with something that feels more like a pleasure than a chore. When you look forward to an activity, it's easier to make it a regular part of your routine.

Set Realistic Goals

Begin with achievable goals. If you're new to exercise, start with 10 to 15 minutes a day, gradually increasing the duration and intensity as you become more comfortable and confident. The American Diabetes Association recommends 150 minutes of moderate-intensity aerobic activity per week, spread over at least three days, with no more than two consecutive days without exercise. Breaking this down into manageable chunks can help make it feel more achievable.

Incorporate Variety

A mix of different types of exercise can help keep things interesting and maximize health benefits. Aim to include:

- **Aerobic exercises:** Activities like brisk walking, swimming, or cycling boost cardiovascular health and help manage blood sugar levels.
- **Strength training:** Using weights or resistance bands twice a week can increase muscle mass, which is beneficial for blood sugar control.
- **Flexibility exercises:** Practices like yoga or Pilates enhance flexibility, reduce stress, and improve blood flow.
- **Balance exercises:** Particularly important as we age, exercises like tai chi can help prevent falls and improve overall mobility.

Listen to Your Body

Monitoring your blood sugar levels before and after exercise can help you understand how different activities affect you. Be aware of your body's signals. If you feel dizzy, shaky, or unusually fatigued, take a break. Staying hydrated and having a small snack handy if your blood sugar levels drop are good practices.

Create a Supportive Environment

Engaging friends or family members in your exercise routine can provide motivation and accountability. Joining a class or group dedicated to a specific activity can also offer a sense of community and commitment. Additionally, tracking your progress through a journal or an app can provide a visual representation of your achievements, keeping you motivated.

Overcome Obstacles

Life can get busy, and finding time for exercise can sometimes feel challenging. Planning your workouts, just like any other important appointment, can help. Consider your energy levels throughout the day and schedule your exercise accordingly. If you miss a session, don't be too hard on yourself. Each day is a new opportunity to get moving.

Embrace the Outdoors

Whenever possible, take your exercise routine outside. The fresh air, natural light, and changing scenery can boost your mood and invigorate your senses. Whether it's a hike in the hills, a jog in the park, or a bike ride along the beach, outdoor activities offer a double dose of benefits by combining physical exercise with the calming effects of nature.

Stay Flexible and Adaptable

Your exercise preferences, abilities, and needs may change over time. Be open to adapting your routine as necessary. If an activity you once enjoyed no longer fits your lifestyle or interests, explore new options. Remember, the best exercise is the one you can do consistently and with enjoyment.

Safety First

Always consult with your healthcare provider before starting a new exercise program, especially if you have existing health concerns. They can offer guidance tailored to your specific needs and help you identify any precautions you should take.

Celebrating Movement

At its heart, exercise is a celebration of what your body can do. It's about movement, expression, and vitality. By integrating physical activity into your daily life, you're not just managing diabetes—you're embracing a lifestyle that promotes lasting health and joy. Let each step, each stretch, and each breath remind you of your strength and resilience.

Stress Management Techniques

Mindfulness involves being fully present and engaged in the moment, aware of your thoughts and feelings without judgment. Meditation, a practice often used to develop mindfulness, can be particularly beneficial. Even a few minutes of meditation daily can help reduce stress levels. Apps and online resources offer guided meditations specifically designed to promote relaxation and stress reduction.

Deep breathing is a simple yet powerful tool for reducing stress. Techniques such as diaphragmatic breathing (breathing deeply into your abdomen) can activate the body's relaxation response, lowering stress levels. Practice deep breathing for a few minutes each day, or whenever you feel stress creeping in.

Exercise is a proven stress reliever. Activities like walking, yoga, swimming, or cycling can boost your mood and reduce stress, in addition to helping manage blood sugar levels. Find an activity you enjoy, so it feels less like a chore and more like a pleasant escape from your daily routine.

Lack of sleep can exacerbate stress, while stress can make it difficult to sleep, creating a challenging cycle. Prioritizing sleep—aiming for 7-9 hours per night—can help manage stress. Establish a calming bedtime routine, reduce screen time before bed, and create a comfortable sleep environment to improve your sleep quality.

Nutrition plays a role in stress management. A balanced diet can help stabilize blood sugar levels, reducing stress on your body. Avoid excessive caffeine and sugar, which can increase stress levels and affect sleep. Instead, focus on whole foods, plenty of vegetables, lean proteins, and whole grains.

Sharing your feelings and experiences with friends, family, or a support group can provide relief from stress. Connecting with others who understand what you're going through, such as a diabetes support group, can offer emotional support, practical tips, and a sense of community.

Managing diabetes can feel overwhelming at times. Setting realistic, achievable goals for your diet, exercise, and blood sugar management can help reduce stress. Celebrate your successes, and be kind to yourself when things don't go as planned. Remember, progress, not perfection, is the goal.

Feeling overwhelmed by tasks and responsibilities can contribute to stress. Effective time management, including setting priorities, breaking tasks into smaller steps, and delegating when possible, can help you feel more in control and less stressed.

Engaging in creative activities such as painting, writing, gardening, or playing music can be therapeutic and reduce stress. Creative expression offers an escape, allows you to express yourself in unique ways, and can bring joy and satisfaction.

Never underestimate the power of laughter and fun in stress reduction. Watching a comedy, playing with pets, or enjoying a hobby can lighten your mood and distract you from stressors.

If you find stress overwhelming or if it's significantly impacting your life, seeking help from a mental health professional can be beneficial. Therapists can provide coping strategies, support, and treatment options tailored to your individual needs.

Incorporating these stress management techniques into your lifestyle can make a meaningful difference in your diabetes management and overall quality of life. Experiment with different strategies to find what works best for you, and remember that managing stress is an ongoing process. By taking steps to reduce stress, you're not just managing diabetes more effectively; you're also investing in a healthier, more joyful life.

13. Conclusion and Resources

Continuing Your Journey

Your relationship with diabetes will evolve over time, as will your understanding of how best to manage it. Advances in medical research may introduce new insights or treatments, while your personal preferences, lifestyle, and health needs may also change. Stay open to learning, adapting, and evolving your approach to diabetes management. Regular consultations with your healthcare team can help you navigate these changes effectively.

There will be days when managing diabetes feels more challenging. Unexpected fluctuations in blood sugar levels, dietary slip-ups, or simply feeling overwhelmed are all part of the journey. Cultivate resilience by acknowledging these moments, learning from them, and gently guiding yourself back on track. Your journey is defined not by temporary setbacks but by your continued commitment to your health and well-being.

You are not alone on this journey. A community of individuals shares your experiences, challenges, and triumphs. Engaging with diabetes support groups, whether online or in person, can provide a sense of belonging, understanding, and shared purpose. These communities are invaluable resources for encouragement, advice, and companionship.

Managing diabetes extends beyond diet and exercise; it's also about prioritizing your overall well-being. This includes self-care practices that nurture your mental and emotional health. Whether it's through meditation, spending time in nature, pursuing hobbies, or simply allowing yourself moments of rest, these practices are essential components of your diabetes management plan.

Become an advocate for your health by staying informed about the latest diabetes research, treatments, and resources. Don't hesitate to ask questions, seek second opinions, or advocate for the care and support you need. Your voice is a powerful tool in managing your diabetes and ensuring that your care aligns with your values and health goals.

Remember to celebrate your journey and the strides you've made in managing your diabetes. Each healthy meal, exercise session, and positive lifestyle choice contributes to a larger tapestry of well-being. Celebrate the small victories, for they are steps toward a healthier, more vibrant life.

The journey of managing Type 2 diabetes is one of lifelong learning. Continue to seek out new information, whether through books, reputable online resources, workshops, or conversations with your healthcare team. Knowledge is power, and staying informed empowers you to make choices that best support your health.

Above all, nourish hope. Managing Type 2 diabetes is a journey of empowerment, resilience, and hope. It's about more than just managing a condition; it's about living a full, vibrant life. Your diagnosis is just one part of your story, and with each step you take on this journey, you're crafting a narrative of strength, health, and hope.

As you continue on your path, remember that this journey is as much about discovery as it is about management. Each day offers a new opportunity to learn, grow, and thrive. With the right tools, support, and mindset, you can navigate the challenges of Type 2 diabetes and embrace a life filled with health, happiness, and fulfillment. Your journey continues, and with each step, you move closer to the life you envision for yourself.

FURTHER READING AND ONLINE RESOURCES

Books

1. "The Diabetes Code" by Dr. Jason Fung

Explore the underlying causes of diabetes and practical advice on how to prevent and reverse it through dietary changes and fasting.

2. "Diabetes For Dummies" by Alan L. Rubin

A comprehensive guide that covers all aspects of diabetes management in an accessible and straightforward manner.

3. "The Blood Sugar Solution" by Dr. Mark Hyman

Discover functional medicine approaches to prevent and treat diabetes through diet and lifestyle interventions.

Online Resources

American Diabetes Association (ADA)

www.diabetes.org

The ADA website is a treasure trove of information, offering everything from nutritional advice to the latest research and guidelines on diabetes management.

Diabetes Self-Management

www.diabetesselfmanagement.com

Find a wide range of articles on food, nutrition, exercise, health, and lifestyle, as well as diabetes news.

Diabetes.co.uk

www.diabetes.co.uk

A UK-based site offering a global perspective on diabetes management, including an active forum for community support.

Apps and Tools

MyFitnessPal

Track your meals, exercise, and progress over time. The app's database makes it easy to log food intake and monitor carbs, which is crucial for blood sugar management.

Glucose Buddy

A comprehensive diabetes management app that allows you to log blood sugar levels, medication, meals, and physical activity.

Headspace

Stress management is vital in diabetes care, and Headspace offers guided meditations, sleep stories, and mindfulness exercises to help reduce stress and improve overall well-being.

Support Groups and Forums

tudiabetes.org

An online community where individuals with diabetes can share their experiences, seek advice, and find support from peers.

Reddit - r/diabetes

A subreddit dedicated to discussing all types of diabetes, sharing news, tips, and personal stories.

Nutritional Information

NutritionData (Self.com)

www.nutritiondata.self.com

Provides detailed nutritional information, including carb counts, which can be particularly useful for meal planning and monitoring.

Recipes

EatingWell - Diabetes-Friendly Recipes

www.eatingwell.com

A collection of recipes designed to be both delicious and suitable for those managing diabetes, with an emphasis on balanced nutrition.

Research and Education

National Institute of Diabetes and Digestive and Kidney Diseases (NIDDK)

www.niddk.nih.gov

Offers in-depth information on diabetes management, research updates, and educational resources.

PubMed Central (PMC)

www.ncbi.nlm.nih.gov/pmc

Access a wide range of scientific studies, including research on diabetes, nutrition, and exercise.

Continuing Education

Embrace the journey of lifelong learning. The landscape of diabetes management is continually evolving, with new research, treatments, and technologies emerging. Stay informed and curious, and use these resources as a springboard for further exploration. Your proactive approach to learning and self-education can significantly impact your ability to manage diabetes effectively and lead a healthy, fulfilling life.

Remember, the path to managing diabetes is personal and unique to each individual. These resources are here to support you, inspire you, and empower you with knowledge. Whether you're looking for practical tips, scientific insights, or community support, there's a wealth of information at your fingertips. Keep exploring, stay engaged, and let your journey be guided by knowledge, compassion, and the unwavering belief in your ability to thrive.

Support Groups and Communities

The Power of Shared Experience

There's something profoundly empowering about connecting with others who understand the nuances of living with Type 2 diabetes. These communities offer more than just practical advice on managing blood sugar levels or dietary tips; they provide a sense of belonging and understanding. Sharing experiences can validate your feelings, offer new perspectives, and inspire you to persevere through challenges.

Finding Your Community

Communities and support groups come in various forms, each offering different types of support:

- **Local Support Groups:** Many hospitals, clinics, and community centers host regular meetings for individuals managing diabetes. These gatherings offer a chance to meet others face-to-face, share experiences, and sometimes even enjoy guest speakers or educational sessions.
- **Online Forums and Social Media:** The digital age has brought support right to our fingertips. Online forums, social media groups, and websites dedicated to diabetes provide platforms where you can ask questions, share successes, and find encouragement any time of day or night. Websites like tudiabetes.org and social media platforms like Facebook and Reddit have active diabetes communities.
- **Nonprofit Organizations and Associations:** Organizations such as the American Diabetes Association (ADA) and Diabetes UK offer resources, events, and forums for those affected by diabetes. These organizations often host educational workshops, webinars, and conferences that can further deepen your understanding and connection to the community.

Engaging with Your Community

To get the most out of support groups and communities, consider these tips for engagement:

- **Be Open:** Share your experiences, challenges, and successes. Your story might be exactly what someone else needs to hear.

- **Ask Questions:** Don't hesitate to seek advice or clarification on any aspect of diabetes management. The collective wisdom of the community can be invaluable.
- **Offer Support:** Just as you look for support, be there for others. Listening, empathizing, and sharing words of encouragement can make a significant difference in someone's life.
- **Stay Respectful:** Remember, each person's journey with diabetes is unique. Be respectful of different perspectives and experiences.
- **Protect Your Privacy:** When engaging in online forums or social media groups, be mindful of your personal privacy. Share only what you feel comfortable with and be cautious about disclosing sensitive information.

The Benefits of Connection

Engaging with support groups and communities can have profound benefits:

- **Emotional Support:** Knowing you're not alone can help alleviate feelings of isolation and anxiety that sometimes accompany diabetes management.
- **Practical Advice:** From navigating healthcare to finding diabetes-friendly recipes, the practical advice shared within these groups can be incredibly helpful.
- **Motivation:** Hearing about others' successes can motivate you to pursue your health goals and try new strategies for managing diabetes.
- **Education:** Support groups often become conduits for education, offering insights into the latest research, treatments, and management techniques.

Creating Your Own Support Network

If you don't find a group that fits your needs, consider starting your own. With social media and community bulletin boards, creating a space for local individuals managing diabetes or a specific online forum has never been easier. Your initiative could foster a supportive community for others seeking connection and advice.

A Journey Shared

Remember, the journey with Type 2 diabetes is a shared one. Support groups and communities offer more than just advice; they offer companionship, understanding, and hope. As you continue to navigate your path, let these communities light your way, offering comfort, inspiration, and a reminder that you are never alone. In the collective strength, empathy, and wisdom of the community, you'll find an invaluable ally in managing diabetes and living a full, vibrant life.

APPENDICES

A. Glossary of Terms

A1C (HbA1c) Test

A blood test that measures your average blood glucose levels over the past 2 to 3 months. It's a crucial indicator of how well your diabetes is being managed.

Blood Glucose

Also known as blood sugar, it's the main sugar found in your blood and your body's primary source of energy. Managing blood glucose levels is a fundamental aspect of diabetes care.

Carbohydrates (Carbs)

A macronutrient found in many foods and beverages, carbohydrates are broken down into glucose during digestion, influencing blood sugar levels. Understanding and managing carb intake is vital for controlling diabetes.

Diabetes Mellitus

A chronic condition that affects how your body turns food into energy. It's characterized by elevated blood sugar levels due to issues with insulin production or function.

Endocrinologist

A doctor specializing in the endocrine system, which includes the glands and hormones that control metabolism, growth, and development. People with diabetes often see an endocrinologist for specialized care.

Glycemic Index (GI)

A measure of how quickly foods containing carbohydrates raise blood sugar levels. Foods are ranked on a scale from 0 to 100, with lower scores indicating a slower rise in blood glucose.

Hypoglycemia

A condition characterized by abnormally low blood sugar levels, which can cause symptoms like dizziness, sweating, confusion, and, in severe cases, loss of consciousness.

Insulin

A hormone produced by the pancreas that allows your body to use sugar (glucose) from carbohydrates for energy or to store glucose for future use. Insulin helps keep your blood sugar level from getting too high or too low.

Insulin Resistance

A condition where the body's cells don't respond normally to insulin, leading to elevated blood glucose levels. It's often a precursor to Type 2 diabetes.

Ketones

Chemicals your body might produce when it doesn't have enough insulin in the blood and starts breaking down fats for energy. High levels of ketones can lead to diabetic ketoacidosis, a serious condition.

Metabolism

The process by which your body converts what you eat and drink into energy. It's a complex biochemical process that combines calories with oxygen to release the energy your body needs to function.

Neuropathy

A type of nerve damage that can occur with diabetes. It typically affects the legs and feet, leading to weakness, numbness, pain, and potential infection.

Pancreas

An organ located behind the stomach that plays an essential role in diabetes. It produces insulin and glucagon, regulating blood sugar levels.

Prediabetes

A condition where blood sugar levels are higher than normal but not high enough to be diagnosed as diabetes. It's a warning sign and a critical stage for implementing lifestyle changes to prevent Type 2 diabetes.

Retinopathy

An eye condition that can develop in people with diabetes, caused by damage to the blood vessels of the retina. It can lead to blindness if not treated early.

Type 1 Diabetes

An autoimmune condition where the body attacks and destroys the insulin-producing beta cells in the pancreas, leading to a lack of insulin.

Type 2 Diabetes

The most common form of diabetes, characterized by insulin resistance and relative insulin deficiency. It's often associated with obesity and lifestyle factors but has a strong genetic component.

Vascular Disease

A class of diseases of the blood vessels—the arteries and veins of the circulatory system—that can lead to a range of health problems, many of which are strongly linked to diabetes and can lead to heart attack, stroke, or poor circulation.

Weight Management

The process of adopting long-term lifestyle modification to maintain a healthy body weight on the basis of a person's age, sex, and height. Strategies include eating a balanced, calorie-managed diet and engaging in regular physical activity, particularly crucial for managing Type 2 diabetes.

Whole Foods

Foods that are consumed in their natural, unprocessed form, often rich in nutrients. Incorporating whole foods, such as fruits, vegetables, whole grains, lean proteins, and healthy fats, is essential for a diabetes-friendly diet.

Xylitol

A sugar alcohol used as a sweetener. Xylitol is a low-calorie alternative to sugar that has a negligible effect on blood glucose levels, making it a suitable sweetener for people with diabetes.

Yoga

A mind and body practice with historical origins in ancient Indian philosophy. Various styles of yoga combine physical postures, breathing techniques, and meditation or relaxation. For individuals with Type 2 diabetes, yoga can help reduce stress levels and improve overall physical fitness.

Zinc

An essential mineral that has a significant role in the body, including immune function, wound healing, blood clotting, thyroid function, and insulin action. People with diabetes may have lower zinc levels and may benefit from zinc supplementation, under the guidance of a healthcare provider.

B. Substitution Chart for Common Ingredients

Sweeteners

- **Sugar** can be substituted with **Stevia, Erythritol, or Monk Fruit Sweetener** in a 1:1 ratio, adjusting to taste as these alternatives tend to be sweeter.
- **Honey** can be replaced with **Agave Nectar** or **Sugar-Free Maple Syrup**, keeping in mind to reduce the quantity slightly to account for the higher sweetness and adjust liquid content in the recipe.

Flours

- **White Flour** can be replaced by **Almond Flour or Coconut Flour**. Use 1 Cup of almond flour for every 1 Cup of white flour, or 1/3 Cup of coconut flour plus an extra egg to maintain moisture.
- **Whole Wheat Flour** can be substituted with **Oat Flour** in a 1:1 ratio for a gluten-free option.

Fats and Oils

- **Butter** can be substituted with **Avocado Oil or Olive Oil** in baking and cooking. Use a 3/4 measurement of oil for every full measure of butter.

- **Vegetable Oil** can be replaced with **Coconut Oil** in a 1:1 ratio for a healthier fat option in baking.

Dairy

- **Whole Milk** can be substituted with **Unsweetened Almond Milk, Coconut Milk, or Soy Milk** in a 1:1 ratio.
- **Heavy Cream** can be replaced with **Coconut Cream** for dairy-free recipes, using the same amount.
- **Sour Cream or Yogurt** can be replaced with **Greek Yogurt** in equal amounts for a protein boost and reduced fat content.

Proteins

- **Ground Beef** can be substituted with **Ground Turkey or Ground Chicken** for lower fat content. Spice accordingly to enhance flavor.
- **Eggs** (for binding in baking) can be replaced with **Flaxseed Meal** (1 tablespoon flaxseed meal mixed with 2.5 tablespoons water equals one egg).

Sauces and Condiments

- **Soy Sauce** can be replaced with **Tamari** (gluten-free) or **Coconut Aminos** for a lower sodium option, using a 1:1 ratio.
- **Mayonnaise** can be substituted with **Mashed Avocado** or **Greek Yogurt** for a healthier spread or dressing base.

Pasta and Rice

- **White Pasta** can be substituted with **Spiralized Vegetables (zoodles), Whole Wheat Pasta, or Lentil/Chickpea Pasta** for a lower glycemic index option.
- **White Rice** can be replaced by **Cauliflower Rice or Brown Rice** for higher fiber content.

Breads and Baked Goods

- **Breadcrumbs** can be substituted with **Ground Almonds or Rolled Oats** pulsed in a food processor for a gluten-free and lower carbohydrate alternative.
- **Tortillas** can be replaced with **Lettuce Wraps or Whole Wheat Tortillas** for a lighter, lower carb option.

Chocolate

- **Milk Chocolate** can be substituted with **Dark Chocolate (70% cocoa or higher)** or **Cacao Nibs** for less sugar and higher antioxidant content.

C. Nutritional Information Guide

Macronutrients: The Big Three

Carbohydrates

are your body's primary energy source, broken down into glucose (sugar), which your body uses for energy. However, not all carbs are created equal:

- **Fiber**: A type of carbohydrate your body can't digest, fiber helps regulate the body's use of sugars, helping to keep hunger and blood sugar in check.
- **Sugars**: Includes both natural sugars found in fruits and milk and added sugars in processed foods. It's crucial to minimize intake of added sugars to manage blood sugar levels.
- **Starches**: Found in foods like bread, pasta, rice, and potatoes, starches are complex carbs that the body breaks down into glucose.

Proteins

Proteins are the building blocks of your body, used to build and repair tissues, make enzymes, hormones, and other body chemicals. High-quality protein sources include lean meat, poultry, fish, beans, peas, and nuts. Incorporating a moderate amount of protein into each meal can help manage hunger and blood sugar levels.

Fats

Fats are essential for energy, supporting cell growth, protecting organs, and keeping your body warm. Fats also help your body absorb some nutrients and produce important hormones. There are several types of fats:

- **Saturated Fats**: Typically found in animal products and some plant oils, these should be limited to less than 10% of your daily caloric intake.
- **Unsaturated Fats**: Found in foods like avocados, nuts, and olive oil, these are considered beneficial fats that can help improve blood cholesterol levels.
- **Trans Fats**: Found in processed foods, these should be avoided as they can raise bad cholesterol levels and lower good cholesterol levels.

Micronutrients: Vitamins and Minerals

Vitamins and **Minerals** are essential nutrients your body needs in smaller amounts to work correctly. They support various functions, including bone health, immune system function, and blood clotting. While it's best to get these nutrients from food, some people with diabetes may need supplements as recommended by their healthcare provider.

Understanding Food Labels

Serving Size: The first thing to check on a nutrition label; it dictates how many servings are in the container and the nutritional content per serving.

Calories: A measure of how much energy you get from a serving of this food. Managing calorie intake is crucial for maintaining a healthy weight.

% Daily Value (%DV): Indicates how much a nutrient in a serving of food contributes to a daily diet. 5% DV or less of a nutrient per serving is considered low, while 20% DV or more is considered high.

Reading Beyond the Label

Glycemic Index (GI): Although not typically found on food labels, the GI is a valuable tool for understanding how a carbohydrate-containing food affects blood sugar levels. Foods with a low GI value (55 or less) are more slowly digested, absorbed, and metabolized, causing a lower and slower rise in blood glucose.

Sugar Alcohols: Often used in sugar-free and "no sugar added" products, sugar alcohols can still affect blood sugar levels. They are partially resistant to digestion and generally cause a smaller rise in blood sugar than other carbohydrates.

Putting It All Together

Navigating nutrition and food labels requires practice but becomes second nature with time. Here are a few tips to get started:

- Prioritize whole, unprocessed foods to naturally balance your intake of macronutrients and micronutrients.
- Be mindful of portion sizes, especially when it comes to carbohydrate-rich foods.
- Choose foods with high fiber content to help manage blood sugar levels.
- Be cautious of foods labeled "sugar-free" or "low fat," as they can still impact blood sugar levels or be high in calories.

Understanding the nutritional content of your food allows you to take control of your diet and, by extension, your Type 2 diabetes management. This guide is your companion in making choices that support your health and well-being, every step of the way.

Made in United States
North Haven, CT
13 November 2024

60283807R00059